THE
BOTANICAL
TREASURY

Kew

THIS IS AN ANDRÉ DEUTSCH BOOK

Published in 2016 by André Deutsch Limited
A division of the Carlton Publishing Group
20 Mortimer Street
London W1T 3JW

A catalogue record for this book is available from the British Library.

ISBN: 978 0 23300 456 3

10 9 8 7 6 5 4 3 2

Printed in China

Publishing credits:

Kew Project Manager: Lydia White
Additional editorial work: Catherine Bradley, Mark Nesbitt
Picture research: the authors, Catherine Bradley, Lynn Parker, Lydia White
Photography: Thom Hudson, Paul Little
Editors: Gemma Maclagan-Ram, Alison Moss
Design: Russell Knowles, Katie Baxendale
Production: Maria Petalidou

Picture credits:

All images unless otherwise stated © The Board of Trustees of the Royal Botanic
Gardens, Kew. The publishers would like to thank the following additional
sources for their kind permission to reproduce the pictures in this book.
Alecto Historical Editions/The Trustees of the Natural History Museum,
London: 15
Christabel King: 110
Penny Grierson on behalf of the Mary Grierson estate: 154
Lucy T. Smith: 46
Masumi Yamanaka: 54, loose handkerchief tree print.

THE
BOTANICAL
TREASURY

CURATED BY
CHRISTOPHER MILLS
Head of Library, Art and Archives,
Royal Botanic Gardens, Kew

Kew Royal Botanic Gardens

ANDRE
DEUTSCH

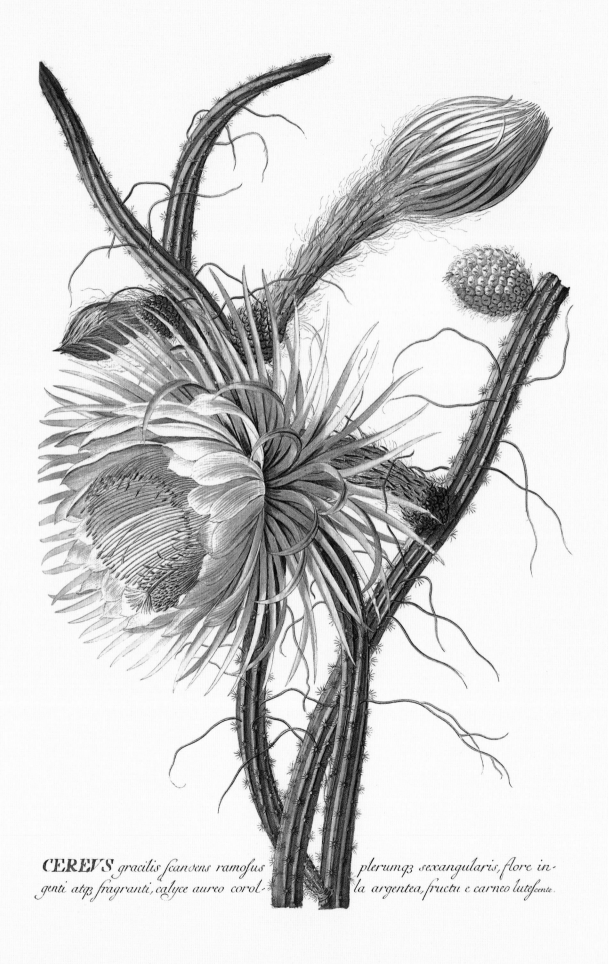

CEREVS *gracilis scandens ramosus* .... *plerumqʒ sexangularis, flore in-*
genti atqʒ fragranti, calyce aureo corol- .... *la argentea, fructu e carneo lutescente.*

PUBLISHER'S NOTE

The classification of plants is constantly being amended with the
advancement of scientific research. We have used a mixture of old
and new names. The new names have been used in cases where it was
felt that some confusion might arise; otherwise, the original names
have been maintained in keeping with the period in which they were
discovered or were illustrated.

ACKNOWLEDGEMENTS

The Royal Botanic Gardens, Kew would like to thank the following
people for their help with the editorial development of this book:
Sophie Burgham, Katherine Harrington, Helen Hartley, Jemma
Magrath, Daphne Maryanka, Taffy Schneider, Brian Schrire, Georgie
Smith, Lorna Terry, and special thanks goes to all of the contributing
authors, the staff of Kew's Library, Art and Archives, especially Lynn
Parker and Julia Buckley, and the Global Plants Initiative.

CONTENTS

INTRODUCTION

Without plants for food, humankind would not exist. So it is not surprising that as we evolved from the instinctive to the discerning, we have developed alongside our nutritional reliance a great fascination with finding new plants, determining the many uses to which they lend themselves and identifying precisely all the plants with which we share our planet. For some, this endlessly intriguing study may almost become an obsession. Plants have also been, and still are, a major inspiration and iconic in many forms of creative endeavour.

Plants feature prominently in the earliest artistic and written records. Images in the tombs and temples of the Egyptian and Minoan civilisations are so finely drawn that we can identify even the species of the plant portrayed. Botanical references appear in ancient Indian, Chinese and Greek texts, giving considerable detail on these civilisations' medicinal use of plants. Probably the most famous of these is Dioscorides' *De Materia Medica*, written in the 1st century AD. A copy dating from AD 512, known as the *Codex Vindobonensis*, still survives in Vienna.

In spite of this long history of collecting and identifying, we still do not know for certain how many different species of plants there are in the world. Estimates as to how much of the world's flora we have so far identified vary considerably. An average of the theories on what remains to be discovered would suggest that at least one-quarter, and possibly one-third, of the world's plants remain to be found and described. For fungi the figure is almost certainly much higher. What other botanical treasures await to be found?

Historically this lack of knowledge of who all the members of the plant kingdom are has driven the discovery of many of the plants included in this work. Every one of those featured is extraordinary in some way, be it for its appearance, structure, life cycle, importance as a food, medicinal properties or other economic or aesthetic use. Equally extraordinary and engaging, in many cases, are the stories associated with the discovery of these plants, revealing the lengths to which collectors and growers would go to find and then propagate them. Behind many of the plants looked at in this book are labours of love, the chasing down of a rumour, feats of survival and tales of great

determination. This book showcases some truly fascinating botanical treasures, and their associated stories will surprise and delight.

Since the dawn of the Age of Science the discovery of a plant was, and still is, usually followed by the creation of a detailed description and the dissemination of that information to other scientists. An accurate visual depiction of the plant, revealing its key characteristics, has always been a vital accompaniment to this profile. As more is learnt about a plant's uses, these details will be added to the literature, often generating further pictures to highlight other features. In the pages following, the plants' stories are supported by a wide selection of wonderful images produced over the last 400 years. These paintings, prints and drawings, along with the supporting documents, are all reproduced from originals held in the Library and Archives of the Royal Botanic Gardens, Kew.

The Art and Illustrations Collection in the Library at Kew is comprised of some 200,000 original paintings and drawings, most referred to by the staff as 'plant portraits'. In addition the Rare Books Collection contains many hundreds of thousands of further images of plants – familiar, exotic, small, large, bizarre, fascinating and indispensable to mankind. This collection may be consulted by anyone fascinated by plants, and selections from the collection are regularly exhibited in the Shirley Sherwood Gallery of Botanical Art at Kew.

Human activity now threatens many plants with extinction before we even realise they exist. Today the aspiration to complete the cataloguing of the world's flora has gained, if anything, an even stronger imperative. Unusual, intriguing plants continue to be found, as the age-old desire to unearth new species continues to be a driving force for many people. In another twist so fascinating to botanists, plants we think we know well may suddenly yield their secrets of how they can be of value. By the time you have completed your own expedition through this book I am sure you will have discovered many botanical treasures, and will look with renewed wonder at the plants with which we share our planet.

Christopher Mills

Head of Library, Art & Archives, Royal Botanic Gardens, Kew

L'Angélique.

Angelica archangelica. Linn. Sp. Pl.

Génévieve de Nangis Regnault f.   *Ital. Angelica. Angl. Angelica. Allem. Angelick.*

SWEET HEALER FROM THE NORTH
ANGELICA

JOANNE YEOMANS

The origin of the name angelica is not clear. It has been suggested that it derives from the flowers blooming on the feast day celebrating the Apparition of Michael the Archangel, which fell on 8 May in the old Julian calendar (replaced in 1582 by the Gregorian calendar, circulated by Pope Gregory XIII). However, the name may also have arisen from the plant's medicinal qualities, especially its ability to "cure all". The 17th-century herbalist Nicholas Culpeper explained that the plant gained its name "because of its angelical virtues". The oldest reference to angelica occurs in the Oxford English Dictionary in 1578, but suggested uses of the plant date back much further, to Old Norse law books of the 11th century.

Angelica is a genus with approximately 60 species from the Apiaceae family, which also includes carrot, celery and parsley. It is a biennial or perennial herb that grows approximately 1–2 m (3–6 ft 6 in) tall. The flowers, either white or green in colour, appear in July or August. The dark leaves are large, up to 70 cm (2 ft 4 in) long, and are supported by a hollow stem. Almost all the plant is sweetly fragrant. It is often used decoratively in gardens, due to its striking, architectural qualities and pretty, delicate flowering umbels.

The species *Angelica archangelica* has been used for centuries for its medicinal and flavouring properties. Other species include *A. sylvestris*, a wild form of *Angelica* native to the United Kingdom, and *A. sinensis*, commonly used in traditional Chinese medicine. It is believed that *A. archangelica* survived the last Ice Age, which took place 8,000–10,000 years ago, and that it originates from the Arctic regions of Finland, Sweden, Norway, Iceland and the Faroe Islands. One of the oldest cultivated vegetables in northern Europe, *A. archangelica*'s importance can be dated back to the Old Norse Gulating, one of the first Norwegian legislative assemblies, between AD 900 and 1300.

At this time many people had angelica gardens, and it was a specific offence to steal the plants from private residences.

Angelica archangelica was believed to have magical powers of protection. It formed part of pagan healing rituals and was used by the alchemist and physician Paracelsus during the 1510 outbreak of the plague in Milan. During the Great Plague in England, *A. archangelica* was used as a preventative rather than a cure because of its antiseptic qualities. It is used in Western medicine to treat many ailments, including digestive complaints.

For the Sami people of Sápmi, which today encompasses the Arctic areas of Norway, Finland, Sweden and part of Russia, *A. archangelica* was predominantly eaten as a delicacy and used for medicine. The root was air-dried, probably by hanging it outside, to conserve it throughout winter. Small pieces of dried root were chewed or mixed with tea or coffee to protect the Sami people from colds and diseases brought from outside the group. The Swedish botanist Carl Linnaeus noted the use of angelica as a vegetable on his travels in the north of the country; he witnessed people peeling the young stems "like an apple" and eating it. Linnaeus also reported that it was used to flavour and preserve reindeer milk.

The Danes were among the first to produce and market candied forms of angelica, which reached England in the mid-16th century. *Angelica archangelica* was grown in large quantities in London in the late 19th century for use in candying, and was a favourite ingredient in many recipe books of this time; only candied ginger was more popular. Eating the stem of *A. archangelica* continued to be popular in the Faroe Islands, Iceland and Norway until the early 20th century. Today, *A. archangelica* is grown for commercial use, mostly in Niort in France, and the candied plant is still used to decorate cakes and to flavour gin and liqueurs.

OPPOSITE: *Angelica archangelica* by Geneviève de Nangis Regnault, from F. Regnault: *La botanique mise à la portée de tout le monde*, 1774.

OVERLEAF: *Angelica sylvestris*, from G. C. Oeder et al: *Flora Danica*, 1761–1883.

Flora Danica Tab.MDCXXXIX.

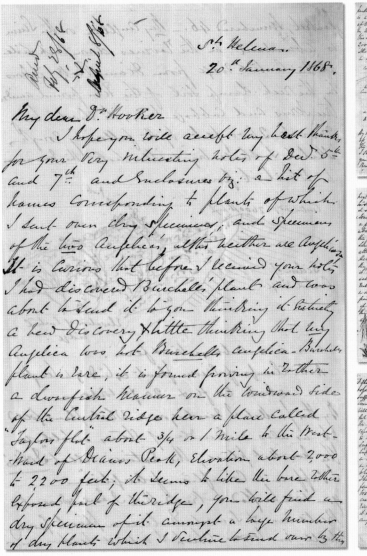

Letter from John Charles Melliss to Sir Joseph Dalton Hooker, from St Helena, 20 January 1868

John Charles Melliss was an engineer and amateur naturalist based on the South Atlantic island of St Helena. Here he writes to Kew's Director Sir Joseph Dalton Hooker, thanking him for his recent letter, plant lists and *Angelica* specimens. Melliss writes about Burchell's plant and *Angelica bracteata* being the same, and explains that it grows abundantly on the island. He includes a sketch of Diana's Peak, the island's highest point, where he describes *Angelica* growing as well as ferns and cabbage trees. He presumes that a plant the indigenous people call *felico* is actually a species of *Angelica*.

Melliss also sends some cabbage trees that he has collected and dried, as well as a species of *Aloe* that grows on the island, possibly Mexican aloe, which he then draws and describes. He ends the correspondence by stating that he will start a plantation of cinchona on St Helena.

1 *Angelica archangelica*, from F.P. Chaumeton: *Flore médicale*, 1833.

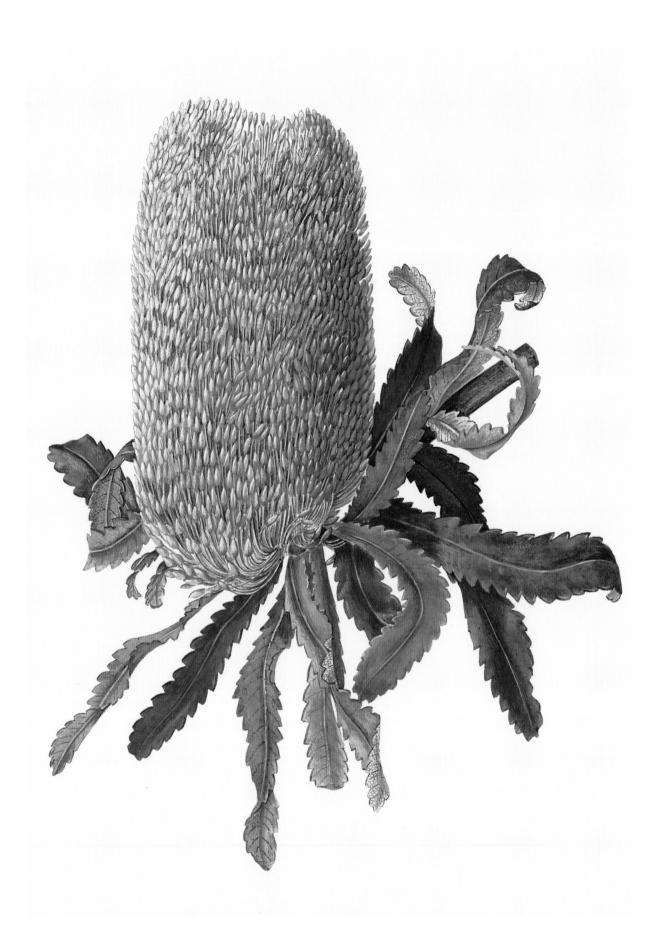

THE BOUNTY OF BOTANY BAY
BANKSIA

CHRISTOPHER MILLS

On 25 August 1768, 94 crew, naturalists and artists set sail from England on board HMS *Endeavour*. So began Cook's First Voyage, an expedition into the uncharted Pacific Ocean tasked with finding the southern land believed to exist but still unknown to the rest of the world. In 1770, Cook's party became the first Europeans to explore Australia's eastern coast and begin to uncover its natural treasures, among them the eye-catching banksias.

An amateur naturalist, John Ellis, wrote at the time to the great scientist Carl Linnaeus that "no people ever went to sea better fitted out for the purpose of natural history". Over the next three years, this expedition, led by the accomplished navigator Captain James Cook, would circumnavigate the world and prove the truth of Ellis's words. Those who survived the journey returned with some 30,000 plant and 1,000 animal specimens, many unknown to science.

A large number of these new species were collected in Australia, and none was more intriguing than those of the genus of plants we call *Banksia*. They were unlike any plants seen before – a wonder to their discoverers and the naturalists of Europe. The very fact that a team of collectors and artists was on the voyage to gather and paint specimens was down to the interest and financial support of Joseph Banks, a wealthy young man passionate to discover the natural world.

Tradition has it that the very first plant that Banks collected after setting foot on Australian soil was a banksia. The *Endeavour*'s landing site became known as Botany Bay, due to the abundance of plants growing there. *Banks' Florilegium* is a stunning visual record of the new plant species found on the voyage, which was finally printed from its 18th-century copper-plates in 1980–90. It features three species of *Banksia*: *dentata* (tropical banksia), *integrifolia* (coast banksia) and *serrata* (saw or old man banksia). These first banksias were described and named by Carl Linnaeus the Younger, the botanist son of the elder Linnaeus, in his *Supplementum Plantarum* of 1781. To show his respect for Banks and his contribution to natural science, Linnaeus the Younger named the genus after him. Today, Banks has about 80 other plant species named in his honour, a mark of his stature in the history of botany.

The *Florilegium* images, along with more recent drawings, have often been reproduced to show the remarkable flower spikes and equally intriguing seed cones characteristic of banksias. Each individual

OPPOSITE: *Banksia serrata* by Stella Ross-Craig, from *Curtis's Botanical Magazine*, 1942.

ABOVE: *Banksia serrata* by Sydney Parkinson, plate 285 for *Banks Florilegium*, 1770. © Alecto Historical Editions/The Trustees of the Natural History Museum, London.

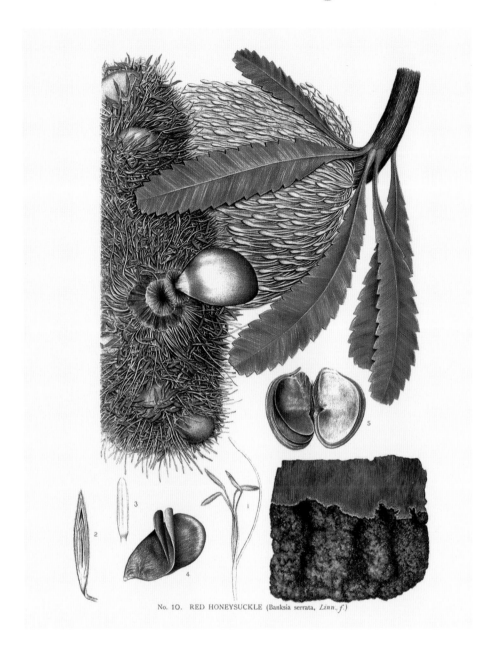

No. 1O.   RED HONEYSUCKLE (Banksia serrata, *Linn., f.*)

LEFT: *Banksia serrata* by Edward Minchen, from J. H. Maiden and W. S. Campbell: *The Flowering Plants and Ferns of New South Wales*, 1895–8.

spike may be composed of hundreds of flowers, but only a few go on to produce fruit. The unusual woody seed cases are composed of two valves that enclose the seeds. When the case splits open it releases one or two small seeds. In all but a few species of *Banksia*, this release is only possible after the plant has been subjected to a bushfire – an unusual adaptation that took scientists years to determine. Many species of *Banksia* have bark that has adapted to help them survive the bushfires essential to their reproduction. Other, more tender species rely on the seed rapidly germinating after a fire to produce a new plant in the fertile conditions left in its wake.

Banksias have continued to fascinate botanical artists, establishing themselves as a popular and technically challenging subject. One of Australia's finest botanical artists, Celia Rosser (1930–), has painted every *Banksia* species. These have been reproduced in *The Banksias*, a splendid large-format work in three volumes which shows the wonderful diversity and intriguing range of this group of plants. Today, there are known to be 170 species in the genus, part of the Proteaceae family. They are found exclusively in Australia and on a few adjacent islands, in a variety of habitats from semi-arid to forest. Banksias range from species that grow as small woody shrubs through to tall trees.

They have also become part of popular Australian culture. The "sinister" seed heads provided the inspiration for the "Banksia men" in May Gibbs's enduringly popular children's book of 1918, *Snugglepot and Cuddlepie.*

First mention of *Banksia*s in Kew's plant *Record Book*, 11 November 1793

Kew has maintained a list of all the plants coming into and being sent out from the Gardens since 1793. The first entry was made on 7 June that year and records that 82 boxes and tubs were received from Botany Bay – "supposed to be a present to the Garden from Governor Phillips". Whilst the entry does not list the contents of the boxes, it is almost certain that such a large consignment would have included some *Banksia* plants and/or seeds. The first item in the *Record Book* that specifically mentions *Banksia*s is that for 11 November 1793, in which plants of four species of *Banksia* (*serrata, dentata, gibbosa, superba*) are listed as having been sent, along with 36 other plants, to Sir Joseph Banks. The *Record Book* details the arrival and despatch of many significant plants over two centuries and evidences how Kew came to assume the role of a "plant clearing house" for the British Empire.

2 *Banksia coccinea* by Ferdinand Bauer, from *Illustrationes Florae Novae Hollandiae*, 1760–1826.

Pub. by S Curtis. Walworth. Jan.1. 1894

ANCESTORS FROM ANOTHER AGE: BAOBABS
ADANSONIA

DAVID GOYDER

*A*dansonia, or baobabs, abound in extraordinary statistics. They are the oldest known flowering plants, the "grandmother" of which, a fony Baobab (*Adansonia rubrostipa*) from southwest Madagascar, has been recently dated to 1,600 years old. A South African baobab (*A. digitata*) is estimated to be even older – an astonishing 1,840 years of age. Not surprisingly, baobabs made a huge impression on 19th-century explorers. Thomas Baines painted the Australian species *A. gregorii* (or boab, as it is known in Australia) on A. C. Gregory's expedition to the Northern Territories in 1855–6. Individual trees painted by Baines on a later journey across northern Botswana in 1861 and 1862 have changed little in the subsequent 150 years, when one compares the paintings to modern photographs.

These trees can grow to enormous proportions, with their massive trunks and spindly branches giving rise to the name of the "upside-down tree". The stately avenue of *A. grandidieri* in western Madagascar consists of trees 25 m (82 ft) in height. In Africa, the circumference of *A. digitata* can exceed 20 m (65 ft), although some such trees consist of several individuals whose trunks have become fused with age.

Six species are native to the Indian Ocean island of Madagascar and occur nowhere else in the world. There is also one Australian species and two now recognized from mainland Africa. The widespread African *A. digitata* has been spread across the continent and beyond by people over many centuries. Arab traders are believed to have established populations of this species in the Majunga area of northwest Madagascar and in India – both regions linked by historic Indian Ocean monsoon trade routes – around the 13th and late 12th centuries respectively. The baobab fruit is still valued highly by many African cultures for its high vitamin C content, and is increasingly traded internationally. Other nutrients present in the fruits are important in the diet of local people. The tree's bark can be harvested for fibre; it has the benefit that its removal does not kill the tree, which can repair the damage to the trunk over time. Kew's Economic Botany Collection includes a net used for catching antelope, made from baobab fibre (see overleaf). It was collected by John Kirk, the botanist and doctor on David Livingstone's famous Zambesi expedition (1858–64), and donated to Kew in 1860.

— 76 —

nouvelles, au moins pour nous. Cependant nous y avons reconnu le gigan-
tesque Baobab, élevant ses puissants rameaux au-dessus de tous les autres,
et les réduisant à ne figurer auprès de lui que comme des buissons.

Lorsque Adanson se trouva pour la première fois en présence du

Fig. 6. Baobab du Sénégal (Adansonia digitata, Juss.)

OPPOSITE: *Adansonia digitata* by William Jackson Hooker, from *Curtis's Botanical Magazine*, 1828.

ABOVE: *Adansonia digitata* by M. Deley, from M. Deley: *La Belgique horticole, journal des jardins et des vergers*, 1859.

Charismatic and stately as these trees are, however, their continued existence in the landscape is not certain. The avenue of *A. grandidieri* at Morondava stands out so spectacularly precisely because the dry forest around it has been cleared for cultivation. Some baobab species have flowers adapted for pollination by bats and lemurs, while other species are pollinated by hawk moths. The loss of many lemur species on Madagascar in the last 2,000 years, since the arrival of man on the island, may have far-reaching effects on pollination and on fruit dispersal. The loss of habitat combined with the effects of grazing livestock means that many populations consist only of mature individuals. Yet baobabs are too important, both culturally and economically, to be lost to the communities that depend on them.

BELOW: Baobab near the bank of the Lue, a tributary of the Zambesi River above Kabrabasi, by Thomas Baines, 1858.

RIGHT: Net made from baobab fibre for catching large game, from Dr Livingstone's Zambesi Expedition, 1860. Kew Economic Botany Collection.

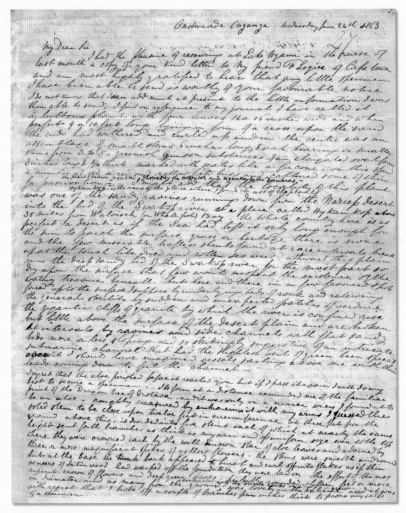

Letter from Thomas Baines to Sir William Jackson Hooker, from Ondweada, Onganga, Namibia, 24 June 1863. First and last pages of 12-page letter.

Thomas Baines writes to Kew's Director Sir William Jackson Hooker to describe his journey through the region from which he and his friend Chapman have forwarded collections and sketches they made as they moved towards Koobie and the Lake country. He describes other specimens he has sent in his collection and discusses a tree which yields a poison known to Dr Livingstone as *ngwa* (its antidote is *kala*). He describes to Hooker the baobab he and Chapman saw at Koobie and writes about the attributes of different types of wood found all the way up to the Zambezi river. They saw a number of baobab and other large trees before they came to the Zambezi and the Victoria Falls. He discusses the different trees seen along the river, including one similar to the baobab which the indigenous people call *kokomboyou*.

He moves on to describe his journey to meet up with Chapman, accompanied by a group of local people, and comments on the tribal and class systems of the area, mentioning in particular the Matabili and Makololo, Makobas, Makalakas, Bushmen and Batoka. He is now staying with Mr and Mrs Andersson, packing specimens, painting and drawing while he raises funds for his next journey, to the east coast via the Zambezi.

3 *Adansonia digitata*, by Thomas Baines, 1861.

THE FRUITS OF PARADISE
BROMELIADS

MARCELO SELLARO

Charles Darwin was fascinated by the Brazilian tropics, which he encountered on the voyage of HMS *Beagle* in 1831–6. En route from Plymouth to Patagonia, the ship crossed the Atlantic and made landfall at Salvador, Brazil on 28 February 1832. Of his first day wandering in the forests, Darwin wrote in *Voyage of the Beagle*, published in 1860: "delight itself, however, is a weak term to express the feeling of a naturalist … the elegance of the grasses, the novelty of the parasitical plants, the beauty of the flowers, the glossy green of the foliage, but above all the general luxuriance of the vegetation, filled me with admiration."

He was neither the first nor the last European to fall in love with the tropical paradise. As early as the 16th century, explorers from Portugal and Spain brought back as many finds from South America as they could. The Europeans were in search of more than gold. Plants were also important in their quest for riches and had significant economic value. Among them were bromeliads, which really enter Western history through Columbus's account of Caribe Indians cultivating the pineapple. This exotic fruit was loved by Europe's aristocracy, and by the mid-19th century it had spread as a crop through many tropical regions.

By then, several botanical gardens in Europe had also started to display other ornamental species of bromeliads. Although bromeliads are related to grasses and sedges, and, like them, have long strap-like leaves, the flowers are strikingly shaped and brightly coloured, appearing highly exotic to the eyes of gardeners in temperate climes. The largest collection of bromeliads was housed in Belgium in the glasshouses of the botanical garden in Liège. It was built up by the botanist Édouard Morren from the 1860s. Morren continued to collect plants throughout his life and was involved in the introduction of new species, such as *Guzmania osyana*, an ancestor of several cultivars well

OPPOSITE: Pine-apple "Lady Beatrice Lambton" by Pieter de Pannemaeker after a drawing by C. T. Rosenberg, *c.*1850.

RIGHT: *Ananus comosus* (as *Ananas aculeatus*) by Georg Dionysius Ehret, from C. J. Trew and G. D. Ehret: *Pantae selectae*, 1754.

known in garden centres. After Morren's early death in 1886, at the age of 53, his manuscripts and drawings were sold to Kew, where they remain in the library today.

You cannot talk of Brazilian bromeliads without mentioning the landscape architect and artist Roberto Burle Marx. He was one of the first to champion the bromeliads' ornamental value in tropical gardens. Marx worked tirelessly to ensure that the plants were not only valued for their looks, but that their habitat was appreciated too. He highlighted the value of using native plants both in landscape design and as a tool for conservation. He once observed that "smooth or hairy, silvery or vividly coloured against the light … some bromeliads give us the impression that they were once sea anemones and jellyfish, or falling stars caught in the treetops" (*Bromeliads in the Brazilian Wilderness*, 1993). A man ahead of his time, Marx championed the use of native plants in tropical horticulture as an effective, sustainable and arresting design option.

An extraordinary botanical family, Bromeliaceae has continued to evolve throughout the Americas. It inhabits several different biomes, from the lush Atlantic and Amazonian rainforest to the bright, sandy vegetation of the coastal plain and the arid inland forest of Caatinga, reaching high-altitude grasslands as well as rooting on rocky soils.

The family's crowning glory, so to speak, is the many thousands of species of epiphytic bromeliads. These plants have the peculiar habit of rooting in the crowns of trees in tropical forests, rather than on the ground. Here, they provide for a huge diversity of birds, mammals and insects. The bromeliads probably offer a greater variety of assistance to other creatures, from microorganisms to pollinators, than any other plant family. For example, ants live in air plants (the genus *Tillandsia*) and birds nest in the trailing tangle of foliage. Bromeliad rosettes are shaped so as to capture rainfall, and frogs use this miniature pool as a nursery to raise their young, as well as an area in which to mate and take cool dips. Indigenous people use fibres extracted from the leaves of bromeliads to make everything from ropes to rugs, further illustrating the ecological and economical importance of the Bromeliaceae family.

BELOW: *Ananas bracteatus,* from *Curtis's Botanical Magazine*, 1858.

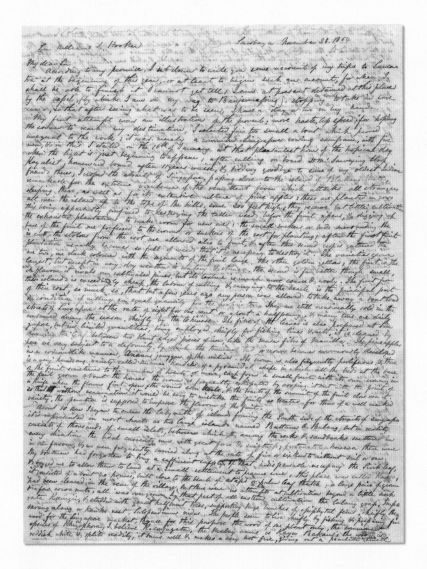

First page of a seven-page letter from James Motley to Sir William
Jackson Hooker, from Surabaya, Indonesia, 28 November 1854

Motley writes from his ship, on the way to Banjarmasin, Indonesia, to
provide accounts of his trips to Sumatra at the beginning of the year.
He recalls his first attempt to reach Sumatra in a Singapore rowing
sampan and comments on the "ananas janggar" pineapples grown on
the island of Blakang Mati (Sentosa). Local villagers trade in a variety
of products including a species of deer, parrots, worms considered a
delicacy by the rich Chinese, and pepper fruit sold on threads to take
to sea. Motley provides a lengthy description of the geology, flora and
fauna he encountered on sailing through the archipelago. Upper parts
of the islands are characterized by Motley as "covered with the usual
jungle trees", including plants yielding Indian rubber and latex. The
archipelago is a Dutch possession, forming part of the Residency of
Rhio, but the petty chiefs are virtually independent and there is little
active government. The island settlements are scattered and retain
"piratical propensities"; the most notorious of the Malay robbers,
known as Hamet, is a native of Boo-oo island.

4 *Ananas comosus*, from M. S. Merian:
*De metamorphosis insectorum
Surinamensium*, 1705.

BARREL-CACTUS
FEROCACTUS HAMATACANTHUS

DANIELA ZAPPI

Ferocactus hamatacanthus is a cactus species that occurs in Mexico in the deserts of the northeast, and in adjacent parts of the United States, in New Mexico and Texas. The genus *Ferocactus* has 16 species and has been subdivided into two sections based on fruit and seed characters. The first, *F.* sect. *Ferocactus*, has dry fruits with a pore at the bottom and microscopically pitted seeds. *F.* sect. *Bisnaga* includes plants with fleshy fruits without a basal pore and with smooth, not pitted, seeds. Among them is the species featured here, as well as nine other species of fascinating barrel-cacti.

Many globose, spiny cacti are known in Mexico as *biznagas*, a generic name that means toothpick and refers to their sharp spines. This term is a Spanish import from the popular name of a plant in the carrot family (Apiaceae), *Ammi visnaga*. Its rigid, spiny inflorescences were used literally as toothpicks in the past. *Biznaga-de-limilla*, the most delicious of the popular names of *F. hamatacanthus*, refers to its small green, sweet-and-sour fruits. Resembling little limes, the fruits are harvested and eaten by locals in northern Mexico.

The North American name "barrel-cactus" is broadly applied to the species of two distinct genera (*Echinocereus* and *Ferocactus*). It describes the plant's shape and size, while "fish-hook" refers to the central, twisted spine of this species. This distinctive spine sometimes helps the plant to tag on to plants or surfaces when blown about by strong desert winds.

Cacti are an almost exclusively American group of plants. As an adaptation for life under harsh desert conditions, the majority of species have no leaves. Instead, photosynthesis, the process of producing sugar for growth and life, is performed by the green tissues in the plant stem.

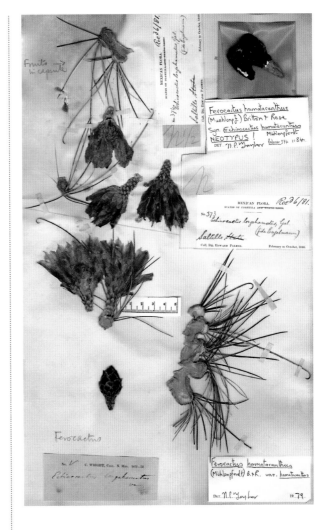

OPPOSITE: *Ferocactus hamatacanthus* (as *Echinocactus longihamatus*) by Walter Hood Fitch, from *Curtis's Botanical Magazine*, 1852.

RIGHT: Kew Herbarium specimen of *Ferocactus hamatacanthus* collected in Mexico by Charles Wright, 1851.

Water storage (another major concern when plants depend on yearly downpours to maintain their growth, flowering and fruiting) takes place in the spongy, dense and pale stem tissue that resembles the flesh of a melon. The ability of the cactus to absorb large quantities of water during the rainy season is enhanced by a wide network of superficial roots, running just under the sandy soils often found where these plants grow. The storage flexibility is conferred by the presence of accordion-like ribs or "inflatable" protruberances known as tubercles. These enable the plant to increase its volume rapidly, without causing its epidermis to burst under the suddenly increased pressure.

The large yellow, silky flowers produced at the top of the *biznaga-de-limilla* plant are pollinated by bees. The petals, which have excellent sun-reflective characteristics, shine and are visible from far away, attracting insects for pollination. Cactus flowers are delicate structures that transpire more than the sturdy, thick-skinned stems, causing the whole plant to lose water. They are therefore generally short-lived in order to save the plant's valuable water resources.

In order to study plant species, samples taken from living plants are pressed and stored in herbaria. The Herbarium at the Royal Botanic Gardens, Kew stores over 7 million specimens from fungi to seed plants, including pressed *biznaga-de-limilla* plants. An interesting letter written in 1874 by Mr Archer, a gardening enthusiast procuring cacti for Sir Joseph Dalton Hooker, the Director of Kew Gardens, confirms that cactus plants were being shipped to Kew using an "on-board glasshouse", also known as a Wardian case (see below).

The outstanding beauty of cacti, and the wide variety of their colours and forms, has meant that they have often been collected in the wild by horticulturalists. Today, this practice is discouraged because many cacti are endangered. Instead, collectors should cultivate the plants from seed, rather than harvesting them from their habitat.

BELOW: Wardian case, a portable airtight greenhouse developed by Nathaniel Bagshaw Ward, used to ship plant samples back to Kew.

Letter from Alleyne S. Archer to Sir Joseph Dalton Hooker, from Speightstown, Barbados, 13 July 1874

Gardening enthusiast Archer reports to Hooker that he has procured plants of the Turk's-head cactus (*Ferocactus hamatacanthus*), some of which he has potted and will keep until next spring, when he will pack them in Wardian cases to send. As Hooker is very anxious for the cacti, he will also send a Wardian case full via the barque *Candidate,* leaving Barbados this week, consigned to Messrs Thomas Daniel & Co. of Mincing Lane. The cacti only reached Archer from St Kitts a day or two before, and, therefore, he cannot ensure that they will grow. Archer notes the finest specimens in the West Indies are procured from the island of Barbuda and that even in Barbados they appear to stop growing after being removed from their native habitat. He would like a few plants before the winter sets in if possible, but asks if Hooker can avoid sending them by Royal Mail steamer since its charges for freight are much greater than those of the Liverpool Line.

5 *Ferocactus hamatacanthus* (as *Echinocactus longihamatus*), from K. Schumann: *Bluhende Kakteen,* 1900–21.

901

Off. lith. & pict in Horto Van Houtteano

CAMELLIA JAPONICA

A BEAUTY FROM THE EAST
CAMELLIA

KIRI ROSS-JONES

his beautiful plant, with its glossy evergreen foliage and jewel-like blooms, is an attractive feature of many gardens. It was named in 1735 after Georg Joseph Kamel, a Jesuit missionary and botanist mistakenly attributed with having brought the first camellia plants to Europe. Today, there are almost 250 species of *Camellia*, all with flowers that are predominantly a shade of red, pink or white. Although the plant was originally grown under glass in Britain, many species are hardy and well suited to a lightly shaded, sheltered spot in the garden. Camellias require acid soil, which is formed in their natural forest habitat by rotting leaves, but they will grow happily in a container in areas with more alkaline soil. Most varieties flower in spring, but some bloom in winter, providing interest when much of the rest of the garden is dormant.

Native to Japan, China and mainland Southeast Asia, camellias were first introduced to Europe in the late 17th or early 18th century. In England, the aristocracy at first grew their camellias in hothouses, anxious to protect their rare and valuable oriental specimens. At Chatsworth House, Derbyshire, in 1838, the Duke of Devonshire commissioned Joseph Paxton, his head gardener, who later designed London's Crystal Palace, to build a glass structure to house his camellia. It was later discovered that most camellias were in fact hardy. From the late 18th century, as trade with the Far East opened up and an interest in all things oriental emerged, new species of camellia were brought to England.

Described by *Curtis's Botanical Magazine* in 1788 as "the most beautiful tree", the camellia is also closely related to the tea beverage. Of the 62 billion cups of tea drunk in Britain every year, all are produced from one of two camellia varieties: *Camellia sinensis* var. *sinensis* or *C. sinensis* var. *assamica*. Such use of the camellia has a long history; there is some evidence of prehistoric use of tea, and Chinese legend ascribes the first taste of tea to the Emperor Shen Nung in 3000 BC. By the 7th century AD, tea was a part of Chinese daily life, both as a medicinal plant and as an aid to meditation for Buddhist monks, who carried their practices and the plant to Japan. Tea did not reach Europe until the late 16th or early 17th century; the diarist Samuel Pepys mentioned his first drink of "tee (a China drink)" in 1660. Initially expensive, and thus the preserve of the upper classes, the

OPPOSITE: *Camellia japonica,* from L. van Houtte: *Flores des serres et des jardin de l'Europe*, 1845.

ABOVE: *Camellia japonica* by Pierre Joseph Redouté, from P. J. Redouté: *Choix des plus belles fleurs et des plus beaux fruits*, 1833.

beverage became more widely available by the 18th century. The East India Company strengthened its hold on trade with China at this time, trading opium grown in its Indian colonies in return for the Chinese leaves.

Joseph Banks, the great benefactor of Kew Gardens, suggested that tea could be grown within the British Empire's own lands. Plants were sent to the East India Company's Botanic Garden in Calcutta in the hope of introducing tea to India, but they never flourished. In 1789, Colonel Robert Kyd, the superintendent of the garden, reported to Banks the locals' "aversion to the ever new species of food, however excellent … until habituated by long custom". Thirty years later, wild indigenous tea plants were discovered in Assam, in the north of India, where they were used by local tribes. However, it was not until the East India Company lost its monopoly on trade with China in 1833 that the British administration developed a real interest in growing tea in India. At first, Chinese plants and knowledge, smuggled from China by Robert Fortune, who was employed by the East India Company, were used. However, it soon became clear that the indigenous plant was hardier and better suited to the environment, producing greater yields. India is now the second-biggest producer of tea in the world. And although hundreds of different varieties of tea can now be purchased, from Darjeeling to green, and Earl Grey to Bohea, all come from one of the two varieties of *C. sinensis*.

ABOVE: *Camellia sinensis* by unknown artist, from *The Company School*, late 18th century.

I have been honor'd with a cursory pe-
rusal of the remarks of the President of the Royal Society
on the late institution of the botanical garden in the neighbourhood of Calcutta, which appear to me, to rise from the ground
assumed, and I should readily acquiesce in the conclusion
deducible therefrom, respecting the limits of the institution in
question, if a different view of the subject (accruing probably
from the information afforded by local observation) and
which appears to me unattainable on any other ground, from
the defective statements, and knowledge of the genius and manners
of the people of the east, yet diffused in the western world.

On this principle, I have thrown together
such observations as have occurred to me, and which, if not
improperly expressed, may, under the correction of the Board,
enable Sir Joseph Banks from a further view of the subject,
and with the enlightened grasp of mind which he possesses,
to chalk out a final and permanent plan for bringing it
to as successful an issue, as the means resources and situa-
tion of the British Government in India will admit.

From the Court of Directors transmitting
these remarks without comment or order it may be presumed
they have hesitated to decide on the propriety of their application

best endeavours being exerted, and under the impression
of their not proving, undeserving of success. — That in the
event, either of a favorable or adverse issue, he shall not
look to this Government, but solely to the Court of Directors
for that remuneration which his services may appear to
merit.

I have only to add, that a drawing of
one of the Tea plants received last year from China accompa-
nies this, with a specimen of the leaves prepared by the
Chinese now employ'd in the Company's Garden.

Extract from Colonel Robert Kyd's *Remarks on the President of the Royal Society's Propositions for the Introduction of the Tea Plant into the Company's Provinces, 1789*

In this volume Kyd, superintendent of Calcutta Botanic Garden, considers Joseph Banks's suggestion that tea should be grown in the garden to prevent the "botanical institution" becoming "disgraceful and penniless". On Kyd's recommendation, the East India Company had founded a garden in Calcutta in 1787, to introduce economically viable plants to the region. However the few tea plants received never flourished. In these papers, Kyd writes that he was sending a drawing of one of the tea plants prepared by the Chinese men employed in the company's garden.

6 Original painting of *Camellia japonica* by J. Curtis, from *Curtis's Botanical Magazine*, 1825.

THE QUEST FOR QUININE
CINCHONA

MARK NESBITT

For 300 years, from the 1630s to the 1930s, cinchona bark was by far the most effective treatment for malaria available in the Western world. It still remains of use in acute cases.

Malaria is one of the world's worst diseases: some 200 million cases occur each year and half the world's population is at risk. It has a long history in Europe and Africa and was taken to the New World by European colonists in the 16th century. The disease was widespread in low-lying, damp parts of Britain, such as East Anglia, until the 1950s. Although the biology of malaria was not understood until the early 20th century, its fevers have long been recognized as a medical symptom and have had a wide range of herbal treatments.

The genus *Cinchona* is made up of about 20 species of small trees that grow on the high slopes of the Andes, mainly in Ecuador, Bolivia and Peru. They belong to the Rubiaceae family, which also contains the coffee plant and ornamentals such as *Gardenia*. *Cinchona* is a notoriously difficult group for botanists, partly because the plants of some areas of the Andes are still poorly known and partly because the different species cross easily, leading to hybrid plants. Furthermore, some of the most important characteristics for separating species, such as the texture of leaves, are hard to convey in writing. *Cinchona*'s most attractive feature is its scented flowers, borne at the end of twigs and coloured in shades of red varying from pink to deep purple. The distinctive, long, tubular flower is adapted to pollination by insects such as butterflies.

The active ingredients in cinchona bark are four quinine alkaloids, which kill the *Plasmodium* parasites that cause malaria. Unusually for a herbal medicine, there is no evidence for the use of cinchona bark by the indigenous peoples of the Andes. The bark first came to medical attention in the 1630s, about a century after the introduction of malaria to the region. It was promoted as a cure by the Jesuit order, but Protestant countries such as Britain remained sceptical of its efficacy until the late 17th century.

For 200 years, European pharmacists relied on irregular, highly priced shipments from South America, simply characterized as yellow, red or grey bark. Scientific advances in the first half of the 19th century changed this. Enough botanical specimens had reached Europe to allow a reliable botanical classification of *Cinchona* species, and alkaloids such

OPPOSITE: *Cinchona succirubra* trees on the Madulsima Cinchona Cos Estate, Ceylon (Sri Lanka), 1882.

ABOVE: *Cinchona officinalis* by Walter Hood Fitch, from *Curtis's Botanical Magazine,* 1863.

as quinine could be extracted, identified and quantified by analytical chemistry. In the 1860s this allowed Kew's plant collectors, such as Richard Spruce, to locate and collect seeds of quinine-rich strains of cinchona, after many adventures in the rainforests and mountains of South America. The plants were transferred by way of Kew Gardens to plantations in India. After much experimentation with cultivation and drug production, quinine became widely and cheaply available to both Indian and colonial populations, so saving many lives.

In 1858, a British patent was issued for a tonic water containing quinine. This would have been exceptionally bitter, but soon versions with citrus-fruit extracts and sugar appeared. These more palatable versions now form a key component of gin and tonic, a favoured drink for summer evenings. It is plausible that tonic water first gained popularity in India as a way of consuming one's daily dose of quinine.

Quinine is also effective against leg cramps, and tonic water is said to be especially popular among ballet dancers for this reason.

By the 1930s, effective synthetic anti-malarials had become available, and difficulties in obtaining quinine during the Second World War further stimulated their development. These have now been partly superseded by drugs based on another natural product, artemisin, a traditional Chinese remedy for malaria. However, there is another reason why quinine is regarded with caution by doctors and no longer routinely prescribed for leg cramps: it is toxic, and over-consumption can lead to tinnitus, vertigo and blindness. Medical literature on the subject contains several cases in which the drinking of large quantities of tonic water, with or without gin, has led to serious illness. Careful questioning was necessary to elicit the true and rather unexpected cause.

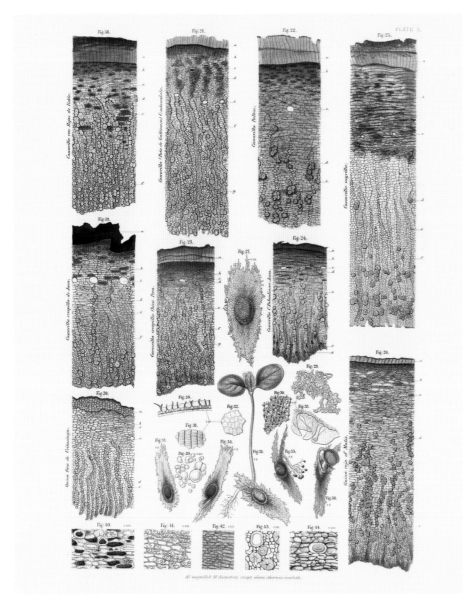

LEFT: Microscopical observations of cinchona bark and seedlings by Walter Hood Fitch, from J. E. Howard: *Illustrations of the Nueva Quinologia of Pavon*, 1862.

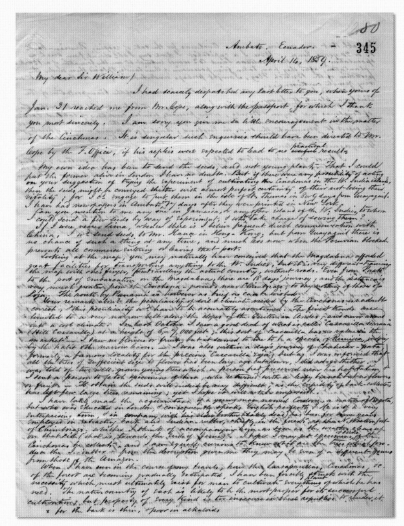

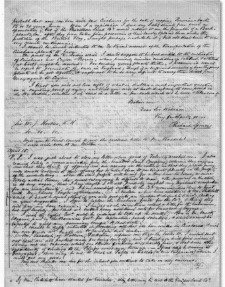

Letter from Richard Spruce to Sir William Jackson Hooker, from Ambato, Ecuador, 14 April 1859

Spruce writes to Hooker to suggest the transporting of the cinchona as seeds, and that these could be sent to the Isle of St Thomas in eight or nine days. The route of the *Magdalena* to the West Indies is not as favourable as it appears, the route by Panama being much quicker. He discusses the environment needed to grow cinchona, the finest quality of which is found in a belt in the Quitonian Andes. Spruce has observed how the forests are "gradually being extinguished", and that any plant needed by man will soon have to be cultivated.

In a postscript dated 15 April, Spruce goes on to add that the Ecuador Land Company has offered him a position in the interior, but it has been vague and he is unwilling to take it up, referring the company instead to Dr James Taylor of Riobamba. He will collect for the Herbarium but it will be limited. He wishes that the British Government would take more interest in the subject and notes that, in contrast, the Bavarian Government has sent Dr Moritz Wagner on a purely scientific exploration of the region.

7 *Cinchona macrocalyx* (as *Cinchona erythrantha*) by Walter Hood Fitch, from J. E. Howard, *Illustrations of the Nueva Quinologia of Pavon*, 1862.

CITRUS Medica.   CITRONIER de Médic.

ORANGES AND LEMONS...
CITRUS

GINA FULLERLOVE

N ative to northeast India, the citron (*Citrus medica*) has been known for many centuries. Its fruit, endowed with many properties, has been associated with religion, magic and medicine; it was first referred to, as *jambila*, in the *Vajasaneyi Samhita*, a collection of religious texts dating from before 800 BC. Virgil gave a poetic description of the fruit and its qualities, and during the reign of Nero, the citron featured in an infamous banquet described in the *Satyricon*, a Latin work of fiction by Petronius.

Its Latin name, *Citrus medica*, given by the famous 18th-century naturalist Linnaeus, indicates the plant's longstanding medical importance. In folk medicine, the citron has been regarded almost as a panacea and used to treat a wide variety of conditions, from colds, gout and heart complaints to relieving the skin and providing an antidote to poisons.

From its native India, the citron spread to Persia in the time of Medes (600 BC). It then spread to Babylonia, where it was used by exiled Jews, who took the plant to Palestine. In 325 BC, the army of Alexander the Great brought the citron to Europe. The Greek writer Theophrastus (*c*.350–287 BC), considered to be the father of botany, described the fruit as the "Persian apple" under the heading "The trees and herbs special to Asia". He notes that it is "not eaten but is very fragrant, as also is the leaf of the tree. And if the 'apple' is placed among clothes, it keeps them from being moth eaten." Early attempts to cultivate the plant in Greece and Italy failed, so the fruits were imported as an exotic delicacy. It was not until the first century AD that the citron was successfully grown in Europe.

The origin and relationships of modern *Citrus* species and varieties, which give us the many fruits we consume today, are complex. Many have only been unravelled recently through hybridization (crossing) experiments and DNA analysis of both commercial varieties and their wild relatives.

The citrus is native to a wide region of Southeast Asia, ranging from sub-temperate China in the north to Australia in the south, where the highest number of species occur. Given such widespread distribution, it has been calculated that citrus ancestry must date back over 20 million years, when the continent of Australia was still joined to Asia. Records of the plant exist in ancient Chinese literature, in the "*Yu*

OPPOSITE: *Citrus medica* by Pancrace Bessa, from H. L. Duhamel du Monceau: *Traité des arbres et arbustes*, Nouvelle édition, 1819.

ABOVE: *Citrus* x *limon* (as *Citrus linonium*) by Pancrace Bessa, from H. L. Duhamel du Monceau: *Traité des arbres et arbustes, Nouvelle édition*, 1819.

LEFT: *Citrus* x *aurantium* (as *Citrus bigaradia* var. *bizarro)* by Pancrace Bessa, from H. L. Duhamel du Monceau: *Traité des arbres et arbustes, Nouvelle édition,* 1819.

Gong" ("Tribute of Yu", part of the *Book of Documents),* dating back to about 2,500 years ago.

The origin of modern citrus begins with the mandarin (*C. reticulata)* from China. This was crossed with the pomelo (*C. maxima),* probably from Indochina, to give oranges and grapefruit (*C.* x *aurantium).* The first crossing gave the type of sour orange used to make marmalade and the flower oil for eau de Cologne. Back-crosses with parent plants produced grapefruit, sweet oranges and tangelo. A Chinese *Monograph of Citrus,* dating from 1178, details 27 varieties of sweet, sour and mandarin oranges, citrons, kumquats and the trifoliate orange.

The lemon (*C.* x *limon)* developed after bitter oranges, and is a cross of bitter orange with citron. From this crossing also comes true bergamot. Oil from its rind is used in scent, hair and tanning oil, and in Earl Grey tea. The lime (*C.* x *aurantifolia)* was produced next, from a cross between the pomelo and perhaps *C. ichangensis* (a plant said to be related to *C. hystrix,* the source of lime leaves in Thai cooking).

In medieval Europe, peel of the rare and expensive sour orange was recommended, powdered and dissolved in wine, to prevent worms and the Black Death. The sweet orange, introduced to Europe *c.*1470, travelled to the Americas directly after Columbus in the 16th century. It spread rapidly, eventually culminating in the world-leading industries of Florida, California and Brazil. Dutch settlers took oranges and lemons to South Africa in the 17th century, and these were introduced, along with limes, to Australia in the 18th century. However, the mandarin was not known in Europe until the 19th century.

Citrus not only contributes significantly to the global food industry; it also has a long association with Western medicine. Citrus oils are antiseptic, and are used in skin cleansers, insect repellents and fungicides. They have also been studied for their antioxidant, anticancer, antiviral and anti-inflammatory properties. The most famous medicinal use of the fruit juice in the West has been to treat the fatal disease scurvy, the historic scourge of sailors, caused by a lack of Vitamin C. Other uses for the juice have been as an aid to weight loss and in contraception. Recent experiments undertaken in the Australian LemonAIDS programme seek to ascertain whether lemon juice can prevent cellular infection with HIV-related illnesses.

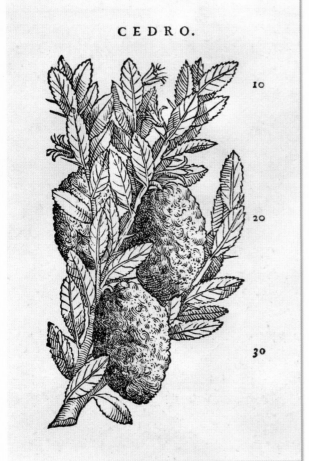

Pages showing woodcuts of citrus fruits from Pietro Andrea Mattioli's *Commentaries on De Materia Medica of the Physician Dioscorides of Anazarba, 1559–1600*

Pietro Andrea Mattioli's *Commentaries* were published in six volumes by the prestigious Venetian press of Vincent Valgrisi (augmented, revised 1559–1660). The *Commentaries* made their author a household name throughout Europe as one of the most famous herbalists of his time.

The work was first written in Italian in 1544, but a Latin edition followed with 562 woodcuts. Fourteen editions were produced by Valgrisi, selling over 32,000 copies. The books were also translated into French, German and Czech. The artists responsible for the woodcuts were Giorgio Liberale and Wolfgang Meyerpeck.

Writings on the medicinal uses of plants have been produced since the dawn of civilization, but *De Materia Medica* by Greek physician Dioscorides (1st century AD) became the most authoritative and influential work for over 1,500 years. The text is systematic and practical in nature, and is considered to be the precursor of modern pharmacopoeias.

Mattioli's *Commentaries* sought to reconcile Dioscorides's writings with the innovations of the Arabs, the medical School of Salerno and botanical discoveries from the Far East, the Americas and Europe. His obsession with the work of Dioscorides is reported to have consumed his every spare moment.

8 *Citrus* x *aurantium* var. *melitense* by Pancrace Bessa, from F. Mordant De Launay and J. L. A. Loiseleur-Deslongchamps: *Herbier général de l'amateur*, 1817–27.

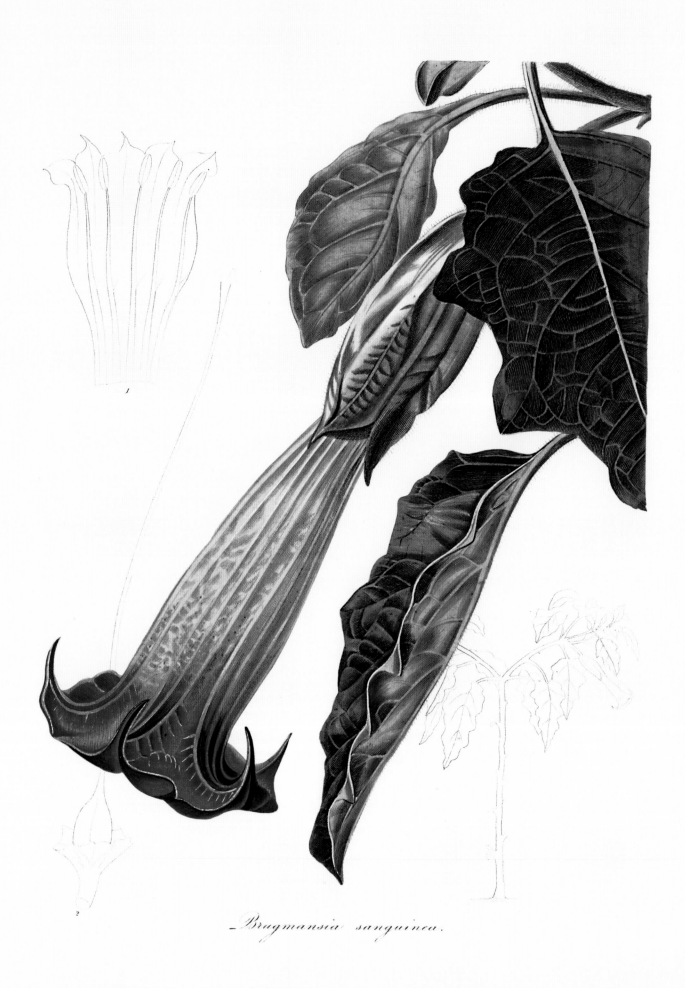

Brugmansia sanguinea.

PLANTS THAT CHANGE BODY AND MIND
DATURA AND BRUGMANSIA

DAVID GOYDER

What comes to mind when you consider members of the solanum family? The humble potato, tomato, chilli pepper or aubergine – or mind-altering hallucinogenic plants? Both angel's trumpets (*Brugmansia* spp.) and the thorn apple (*Datura* spp.) are used medicinally and psychoactively in a variety of cultures around the world.

Both genera abound in the alkaloid chemicals that give the plants their medicinal properties. Several drugs widely used in modern medicine derive from members of this family – atropine, for example, from deadly nightshade (*Atropa belladonna*), is used to dilate the pupil of the eye. So the occurrence of related chemicals in *Datura* and *Brugmansia* is no surprise. As with several other drugs, small amounts may have beneficial medical effects, while high doses can be fatal.

Species of *Brugmansia* in the Andean and Amazonian regions of South America are generally associated with Indian settlements; many have clearly been selected for use in shamanic rituals and are planted around villages. The great Harvard ethnobotanist Richard Evans Schultes and his students built up a huge body of research around the indigenous peoples of the Americas and their use of such plants. From the 1940s onwards, they observed and documented how users of *Brugmansia* were affected physically and psychologically, and even took part in some of the rituals themselves. Schultes and his colleagues could thus describe the – often distressing – psychological effects of these plants from personal experience, with Schultes's major works on the subject published in the 1970s and 1980s. A recent book states that *Brugmansia* species have become extinct in the wild; they are almost entirely dependent on indigenous cultures for their persistence in their native ranges. The main threats to the plant's existence are changing cultural values.

Datura species, too, almost certainly originated in the New World. Some species spread quickly into warmer parts of the Old World as their ornamental and mind-altering properties became appreciated. *Datura* was in widespread cultivation in Europe, South Asia and China soon after European contact with the New World was established, from the 15th century onwards. Descriptions of the effect of repeated ingestion of *Datura* include a sort of drunken behaviour, followed by hallucinations. Further doses induce stupefaction and a complete inability to react to external stimuli. Wade Davis, a student of Schultes, studied African voodoo culture on Haiti. He found that eating a soup made from sweet potatoes and *Datura stramonium* made people behave like zombies or living corpses. When the effects of the alkaloids wore off, many hours later, they returned to normal behaviour, unless the dose was repeated.

Plants of these two genera have large, showy, tubular flowers and are popular in cultivation. In addition to the eight native species of *Datura*, which produce mostly white flowers and the seven species of *Brugmansia*, whose strongly scented flowers range in colour from white to shades of lemon, orange and red, many artificial hybrids and cultivars have been developed. Some of these are a result of ancient cultivation in the Americas. In *Datura*, flowers are held erect, while they are nodding or pendant in *Brugmansia*. There are also other differences: *Datura* is an annual or short-lived plant, whereas *Brugmansia* is a woody shrub. *Datura* generally has a spiny fruit that splits open as it dries, while *Brugmansia* has smooth, fleshy fruit that remain closed at maturity.

OPPOSITE: *Brugmansia sanguinea* by A. I. Withers, from B. Maund and J. S. Henslow: *The Botanist*, 1836.

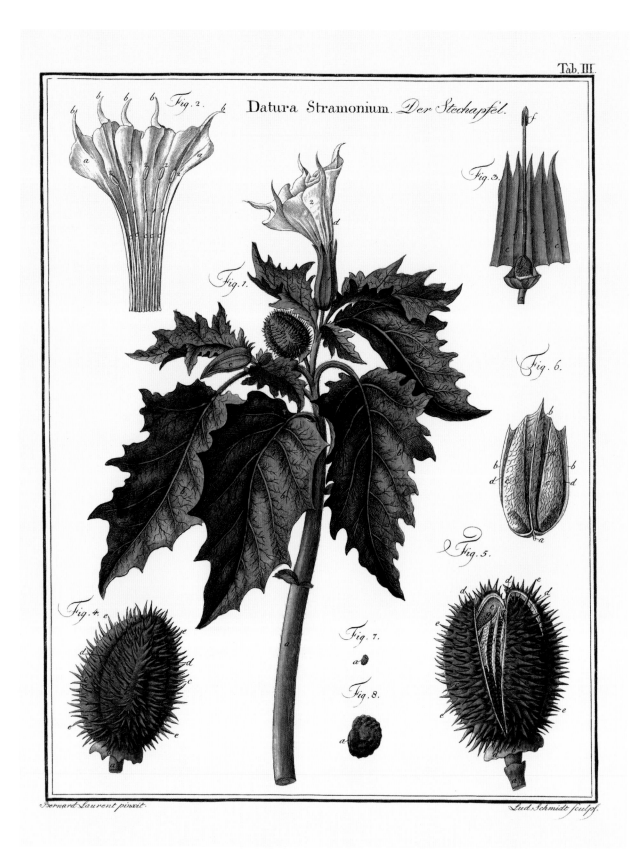

Tab. III.

Datura Stramonium. *Der Stechapfel.*

Fig. 2.

Fig. 3.

Fig. 1.

Fig. 6.

Fig. 5.

Fig. 4.

Fig. 7.

Fig. 8.

Bernard Laurent pinxit.

Lud. Schmidt sculps.

T. 7. N.° 1.

DATURA arborea.   STRAMOINE en arbre.

P. Bessa pinx.   Gabriel sculp.

DATURA.   STRAMOINE.

DATURA. Lin. Classe V. *Pentandrie*. Ordre I. *Monogynie*.
DATURA. Juss. Classe VIII. *Dicotylédones monopétales. Corolle
hypogyne*. Ordre VIII. Les Solanées. §. I. Une capsule pour fruit.

GENRE.

CALICE.   Monophylle, tubuleux, ventru, anguleux.
COROLLE.   Monopétale, infondibuliforme, à tube cylindrique. Le limbe est
un peu campanulé, marqué de cinq plis et à cinq lobes.
ÉTAMINES.   Au nombre de cinq, ayant leurs filamens subulés, plus courts
que la corolle, adhérens à son tube et terminés par des an-
thères oblongues.
PISTIL.   Un ovaire ovale, supérieur, surmonté d'un style droit, filiforme,
plus long que les étamines, terminé par un stigmate obtus,
un peu renflé.
PÉRICARPE.   Une capsule ovale, à quatre loges formées par des cloisons, dont
deux seulement complettes et les deux autres n'allant pas jusqu'au
haut des parois des valves.
SEMENCES.   Réniformes, nombreuses.
CARACTÈRE ESSENTIEL. Calice monophylle, tubuleux. Corolle monopétale, infondibuliforme, plissée. Cinq étamines. Un style terminé par un stigmate obtus.
Capsule à quatre loges incomplettes, contenant plusieurs graines réniformes.
RAPPORTS NATURELS. Avec les genres *Atropa, Physalis* et *Nicotiana*.
ÉTYMOLOGIE. Le mot *Datura* est turc; il a d'abord été le nom de l'espèce la plus
commune, et on l'a donné ensuite au genre entier.

1. DATURA arborea. *Tab.* 1.   STRAMOINE en arbre. *Pl.* 1.
D. *caule fruticoso; foliis ovato-lanceolatis,*   S. à tige frutescente; à feuilles ovales-lancéo-
oblongisque; floribus nutantibus; corol-   lées et oblongues; à fleurs pendantes, ayant
larum lobis acuminatis; capsulis ovato-   les lobes de leur corolle acuminés; à cap-
oblongis, glabris, inermibus.   sules ovales-oblongues, glabres et dépourvues
de piquans.

DATURA arborea. Lin. Sp. 256. Willd. Sp. 1. p. 1009. Ruiz et Pav. Fl. Peruv. p. 16.
t. 128. Poir. Dict. Enc. 7. p. 463.
BRUGMANSIA candida. Pers. Synop. 1. p. 216.
Stramonioïdes arboreum, oblongo et integro folio, fructu levi. Feuillée Peruv. 2. p. 761. t. 46.

La Stramoine en arbre, nommée vulgairement *Trompette du jugement*, est un
arbrisseau qui peut s'élever dans nos jardins à la hauteur de huit à dix pieds, et dont
les tiges sont droites, cylindriques, divisées en rameaux étalés. Ses feuilles sont
pétiolées, géminées, ovales-lancéolées ou oblongues, glabres en dessus, couvertes
en dessous de poils très-courts, très-nombreux, et seulement visibles à la loupe:
selon Feuillée, ces feuilles sont cendrées et pulvérulentes dans leur pays natal. Les
fleurs sont axillaires, pédonculées, pendantes; elles pendant, surtout le soir, une
odeur agréable. Leur calice est à cinq dents; leur corolle est blanche, l'une des
plus grandes que l'on connaisse, ayant neuf à dix pouces de longueur sur cinq à six
pouces de largeur; ses lobes sont peu prononcés, si ce n'est par la pointe assez longue

7.   A

Pages from Henri Louis Duhamel du Monceau's *Traité des arbres et arbustes que l'on cultive en France en pleine terre* (second edition), early 19th century

The above description of the *Datura* genus from *Traité des arbres et arbustes que l'on cultive en France en pleine terre* was published in Paris in the early 19th century. This technical handbook on trees and shrubs was one of the many botanical works of Henri Louis Duhamel du Monceau (1700–82), a French landowner who conducted experiments in horticulture, agriculture and forestry on his large estate. He published the results from his model farm in numerous publications and was elected to the French Academy of Sciences in 1738. He became its president three times.

Duhamel's early work included exploration into problems with saffron-growing in Gâtinais (an area of France between the rivers Seine and Loire), which he traced to a parasitical fungus that caused disease. He undertook many experiments in plant physiology, including studies on the growth and strength of wood, the growth of mistletoe and the effects of planting in layers, as well as the impact of meteorological conditions on agriculture. He also became Inspector-General of the Marine in 1739, where he carried out scientific studies on shipbuilding and the conservation of wood.

OPPOSITE: *Datura stramonium* by Bernard Laurent, from J. C. A. Mayer: *Einheimische Giftgewächse welche fur Menschen am schädlichsten sind*, 1798–1801.

Datura cornucopaea, from W. Robinson: *The Garden. An illustrated weekly journal of horticulture in all its brances*, 1894.

SEED PLANTS FROM THE DAWN OF TIME
ENCEPHALARTOS

ALJOS FARJON

*E*ncephalartos is a genus of African cycads – plants that look like palms but are actually gymnosperms, non-flowering seed plants. In geological records, they have existed for a very long time, and were prominent throughout the Mesozoic Era, the age of the dinosaurs, *c.*210–65 million years ago.

The cycads are a group of primitive seed plants. They mostly occur in the tropics and subtropics of Central and South America, Africa, Southeast Asia and Australia, as well as on some islands in the Caribbean and western Pacific Ocean. In the Mesozoic Era, the climate was generally warmer than it is now, and cycads would have grown at higher latitudes as well. *Encephalartos* has 65 species and occurs in sub-Saharan Africa in the tropics and in the Eastern Cape of South Africa. Apparently, they evolved after Africa became separated from South America, where other cycads are found. Many species are now rare, and typically exist in small populations. The most extreme example of this is *Encephalartos woodii*, of which only a single male plant is left "in the wild" in South Africa. Although, it has made offsets, some of which have been grown in botanic gardens, we will never have seeds of this species.

Cycads have some very primitive traits, such as motile sperm, but are also advanced in comparison with other gymnosperms. This is because they are pollinated by beetles, not by wind as are their relatives the conifers. Female and male plants are separate, and in *Encephalartos* both form large cones. The female cones of *E. longifolius*, the biggest of any cone-bearing plant, with seeds as big as plums, can weigh up to 40 kg (88 lb). In the male cones, which produce the pollen, heat can be generated that is up to 17°C (30.6°F) warmer than the air temperature

OPPOSITE: *Encephalartos altensteinii* in Kew's Palm House by Lucy T. Smith, 2006. © Lucy T. Smith.

RIGHT: *Encephalartos horridus* by Walter Hood Fitch, from *Curtis's Botanical Magazine*, 1863.

outside. Beetles seek this warmth when it cools off at night, and then fly out, bearing pollen, in the daytime.

Some of the species, with their viciously sharp, pointed leaflets on fronds (which do indeed resemble palms and is probably why another name for the cycad is bread palm), look likely to have deterred even the toughest dinosaur mouth. Perhaps they did, but cycads have a weak spot in this respect. In contrast to palms, the new leaves come in a flush at irregular intervals all at once, and these are surprisingly soft – even those of the very spiny species such as *E. horridus*, whose name alone sounds like a deterrent! So dinosaurs may have fed on cycads after all. Nowadays, however, they are mostly toxic and few animals eat them. *Encephalartos ferox* is another species with armoured leaflets.

A famous specimen at the Royal Botanic Gardens, Kew is reported to be the oldest greenhouse plant in the world, and is certainly the oldest in the UK. The plant is prostrate because its trunk has continued to grow since being put in a pot some 240 years ago. Francis Masson collected it as a small plant in 1773. It arrived at Kew in 1775 and was first described as *Zamia longifolia*, later transferred to *Encephalartos* when that genus was erected. So it should now be known as *E. longifolius*, but in Kew's Palm House it is labelled as *E. altensteinii*. Two large plants were described by Joseph Hooker in *Curtis's Botanical Magazine* of 1856 (see opposite); he called them *E. caffer*, now a synonym of *E. longifolia*. One of these plants already had a stem of 2.4 m (8 ft) and was very likely our present ancient plant. In the most recent scientific *Checklist of the Cycads* both species are recognized, so it seems that we need to amend the label as others concur.

BELOW: *Encephalartos hildebrandtii* growing in Kew's Palm House, 1901.

TAB. 4903.

ENCEPHALARTUS CAFFER.

Caffrarian Encephalartus, or Caffer-bread.

Nat. Ord. CYCADEÆ.—DIŒCIA POLYANDRIA.

Gen. Char. FLORES MASCULI :—*Antheræ* apertæ, in strobilum terminalem pedunculatum collectæ, undique rachi communi insertæ, singulæ oblongo-cuneatæ, apice incrassato-obtusæ v. acuminatæ, acumine sursum flexo, connectivo plus minus distincto. FLORES FŒMINEI :—*Carpidia* plurima, monophylla, aperta, in strobilos terminales pedunculatos collecta, rachi communi undique inserta, singula basi in stipitem attenuata, apice in peltam rhomboideam dilatata, pelta subtus utrinque ovulo unico inverso fœta. *Fructus* syncarpius, e carpidiis laxiuscule coalitis. *Semina* ovoidea, *testa* ossea, sæpius carpidii processu fungoso cupulatim excepta. *Embryo* inversus, in axi albuminis carnosi, *radicula* respectu racheos communis centripeta.—*Arbores, interdum giganteæ, in* Africa australi *subtropica (regione Caffrarum)*, frondibus *pinnatis*, pinnis *lata basi sessilibus*, *multinerviis*, apice *sæpius spinoso-denticulatis. Endl.*

ENCEPHALARTUS *Caffer*; caudice erecto glabro tereti-cylindraceo elato, foliis (cum petiolo) subtripedalibus apice recurvis circumscriptione lanceolatis pinnatis glabris, pinnis utrinque sub-37 erecto-patentibus anguste lanceolatis coriaceis rigidis atro-viridibus (minime glaucis) planiusculis supra nitidis estriatis subtus minute longitudinaliter striatis, margine paululum recurvis integris vel uni- vel remote- bi-tridentato-spinosis, inferioribus latioribus apice mucronato-spinosis reliquis mucrone obtuso recurvo terminatis, rachi glabra obtuse inequaliter subtetragona, amento masculo subcylindraceo sesquipedali, squamis antheriferis oblongis glabris tuberculoso-rugosis apice rostrato, rostro decurvo truncato.

α. foliolis omnibus integerrimis. (TAB. NOSTR. 4903.)
β. foliolis hic illic remote dentato-spinosis.
ENCEPHALARTUS Caffer. *Lehm. Pugill. v.* 6. *p.* 11. *Miq. Monogr. Cycad. p.* 53.
CYCAS Caffra. " *Thunb. Nov. Act. Reg. Soc. Ups. tom.* 2. *p.* 283."
ZAMIA Cycadis. *Linn. Fil. Suppl. p.* 443. *Ait. Hort. Kew. ed.* 2. *p.* 412.
ZAMIA Caffra. *Thunb. Fl. Cap. ed. Schult. p.* 429.
ENCEPHALARTUS longifolia. *Lehm. Pugill. v.* 6. *p.* 14. *Miq. l.c. p.* 54.

A desire to give a local habitation and a name, if possible, to this noble Cycadaceous plant, of which we have received at Kew splendid living specimens from various friends, our finest from J. Moxon, J. Brehem, and — Ariderne, Esqs., from the neighbourhood of Graham's Town, induce me to give a representation from imperfect materials,—imperfect from the absence of fruit-bearing amenta, in which probably the most dependable distinguishing characters will be found to reside. Of the species to which it belongs, I would desire to speak with great caution ; and
MARCH 1ST, 1856.

Fitch del et lith.   Vincent Brooks Imp.

Article describing *Encephalartos caffer* written by Joseph Dalton Hooker for *Curtis's Botanical Magazine*, 1856

Hooker praises the "splendid living specimens" of "this noble Cycadaceous plant" that had been received at Kew. Hooker's description is accompanied by a drawing from Walter Hood Fitch, a highly regarded botanical artist for the magazine.

Three hand-coloured engravings featured in the first edition of *The Botanical Magazine*, and high-quality botanical illustrators contributed to its success. The first artists were William Kilburn, James Sowerby and, later, Sydenham Edwards. In 1827 William Hooker, then Professor of Botany at Glasgow, became editor of the magazine and invited Fitch, a young Scottish artist, to work for him.

Fitch became *The Botanical Magazine*'s principal artist, creating over 2,700 illustrations. After William Hooker became the first Director of the Royal Botanic Gardens, Kew in 1841, he made Fitch the sole artist for all publications, paying him personally. Fitch created 500 plates for Hooker's *Icones Plantarum* (1836–76), as well as four lithographic plates for his monograph *Victoria Regina*.

Fitch was initially also favoured by Joseph Dalton Hooker, who described him as an "incomparable botanical artist" when he succeeded his father as editor (and Director of Kew) in 1865. Later the two men had disagreements, and Fitch resigned in 1878.

10 *Encephalartos altensteinii* by Matilda Smith, from *Curtis's Botanical Magazine*, 1891.

Fritillaire Impériale Var. jaune.

P. J. Redouté.

FROM EASTERN MEDICINE
TO WESTERN GARDENS
FRITILLARIA

MARTYN RIX

To Europeans, fritillaries are thought of as rare butterflies, or garden bulbs. Two sorts are familiar to gardeners: the elegant snakeshead *Fritillaria meleagris*, so called because it is spotted like a guinea fowl, and the stout crown imperial *F. imperialis*, with its orange or red bells and round, smelly bulbs, about the size of a small cricket ball. Both of these have been popular garden plants since the 16th century. The former comes perhaps from France, while the latter was brought to Europe from Constantinople, where it was cultivated by the Turks. *Fritillaria imperialis* still grows wild in the mountains of eastern Turkey and Iran.

To the Chinese and Japanese, however, the fritillary, called *bei mu* in Chinese, is one of the most common and popular of traditional herbal medicines. It is used for the alleviation of coughs, colds, phlegm and other ailments of the throat and lungs, and has even been recommended for easing lactation and for breast cancer. The bulbs are collected from the wild wherever they can be found. They are dried and then ground into a white powder before being mixed with water and drunk; nowadays, they can also be bought as factory-made pills. Most Chinese species of *Fritillaria*, of which there are about 20, are used, and in addition to those collected from the wild (the most expensive and sought-after), several species are cultivated in great quantity.

Wild examples are often from remote parts of west and southwest China. In Xinjiang, near the border with Kazakhstan, the most common is the large, green-flowered *F. pallidiflora*. This can reach 20 cm (8 in) in height, with broad leaves and about five yellowish-green bells. In the Himalaya, in Yunnan, Sichuan and Tibet, it is the dark-flowered, coiled-leaved *F. cirrhosa* that is collected in the wild. So valuable was this that Chinese collectors came over the high mountains to find new sources of supply. The famous English plant collector Frank Kingdon-Ward met them digging in the mountains of northern Burma in the 1950s.

One of the most commonly cultivated species in China is *F. thunbergii* – known as *zhe bei mu* in Chinese – a tall plant with smallish, pale-green, lightly chequered bells. One of the first Asiatic species to be described, it was found by and named after the Swedish botanist Carl Peter Thunberg. He sailed to Japan in 1775, and was stationed on Deshima islet near the port city of Nagasaki, an area of

OPPOSITE: *Fritillaria imperialis* var. *jaune* by Pierre Joseph Redouté, from P. J. Redouté: *Choix des plus belles fleurs et des plus beaux fruits*, 1833.

ABOVE: *Friltillaria thungbergii*, from Y. Linuma: *Somoku-Dzusetsu*; or, *an iconography of plants indigenous to, cultivated in, or introduced into Nippon* (Japan), 1874.

フリチルラリフキイヒッブルーム蘭^和

一種

物印滿の圖ふ花紅白相雜るものあり奇品なり

LEFT: Fritillaries by Kan'en Iwasaki
from *Honzu Zufu*, 1828.

just 8,400 sq m (2 acres). Posing as a doctor for the Dutch East India Company (VOC), which then held a monopoly of trade between Europe and Japan, Thunberg took the opportunity to collect, draw and study as many Japanese plants as he could over three years. The Dutch were forbidden to set foot on the mainland, apart from one closely supervised visit to Tokyo each year, but Thunberg persuaded some of the Japanese servants to bring him specimens of garden plants. He also sifted through the hay bought for the animals kept on the island to see if he could find the dried stems or seeds of any new plants.

It is likely that the fritillary stem that Thunberg drew and pressed in 1776 or 1777 came from a local Japanese garden. He called the plant *Uvularia cirrhosa*, as it had no bulb and he did not realize that it was a fritillary. Subsequent generations of botanists recognized it as a fritillary, but, as the name *F. cirrhosa* had already been taken for the Himalayan species, this cultivated Japanese one was named after Thunberg. The Japanese always knew that this was a Chinese medicinal plant, and it is still cultivated in great quantity in China, particularly in the provinces of Zhejiang, Jiangsu and Anhui.

Fritillaria thunbergii is often cultivated in Britain as an ornamental. It grows well in many gardens, but not all, and seems to thrive best when planted under deciduous shrubs, whose leaves keep it cool in summer while their roots prevent it being too wet in winter.

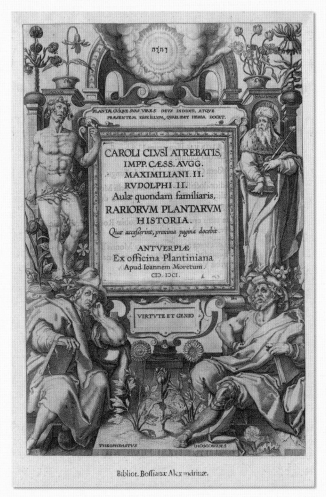

Bibliot. Bossianæ Alexandrinæ.

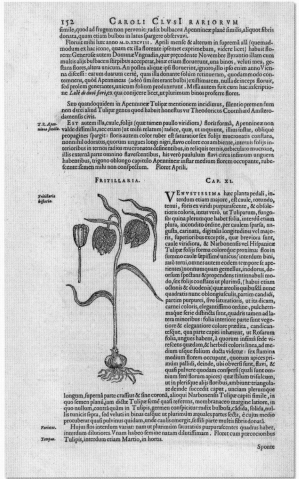

Title page and extract from Clusius's
Rariorum Plantarum Historia, 1601

This page from Clusius's *Rariorum Plantarum Historia* (history of rare plants), published in Antwerp in 1601, gives a typically careful and enthusiastic description of the common snakeshead fritillary *Fritillaria meleagris*, which is such a beautiful sight at the end of April in a few hay meadows from the source of the Thames at Cricklade to Oxford, and was known in the past as far downstream as Kew.

Carolus Clusius (1526–1609) was the foremost botanist of his day, working in Vienna, where he was prefect of the royal medicinal garden under Emperor Maximilian II (1527–76). In 1593 he was appointed professor in the ancient university of Leiden in the Netherlands, where he founded the botanic garden. This has recently been recreated using the plants and layout described in the writings.

> **11** *Fritillaria imperialis* by Pierre Joseph Redouté, from P. J. Redouté: *Choix des plus belles fleurs et des plus beaux fruits*, 1833.

GROWING WITH DINOSAURS
GINKGO BILOBA

JULIA BUCKLEY

Ginkgo is native to China, and venerable specimens can also be found in Japan and Korea. Fossilized remains of the plant have been discovered on every continent, proving that at one time ginkgo grew worldwide. *Ginkgo biloba* is in fact the only existing member of a group of plants stretching back around 200 million years to the Mesozoic Era.

The German botanist Engelbert Kaempfer visited Japan between 1690 and 1692. His *Amœnitatum Exoticarum* of 1712 was the first Western publication to feature a description of *Gingko*, whose title derives from the plant's Chinese name. The genus comprises just a single species, *biloba* – the name referring to the partial split often exhibited in its distinctive, fan-shaped leaves. It was given the common name of maidenhair tree, acknowledging its resemblance to the maidenhair fern.

Ginkgos found their way only gradually into Europe, through tentative trading concessions with Japan in the 18th century. One of the ginkgo trees in Kew Gardens forms part of a set of "Old Lion" trees that were introduced during the reign of George III in the 1760s; this unusual specimen must have attracted great interest when it first appeared. James Gordon's Mile End Nursery was an early purveyor of the tree, and it is likely that Kew's ginkgo came from this source. Originally trained against the wall of a building for protection, the tree proved resilient when the building was subsequently demolished.

The ginkgo is deciduous; its leaves turn a pale yellow before they are shed. It exhibits many unusual characteristics, not least in being dioecious. This means that the trees are either male or female, and must rely on a nearby tree of the opposite gender for fertilization.

The Gardeners' Chronicle of 1882 notes that: "All the female trees in Europe are believed to have originated from a tree near Geneva, of which Auguste Pyramus de Candolle secured grafts." Male trees are favoured for ornamental use, as the "fruits" of the female trees, despite their attractive Chinese name of "silver apricot", emit a pungent and nauseating smell. Rather than fruits in the true sense, these are actually seeds with a fleshy outer layer. In China and Japan, the seeds are removed from their flesh and roasted and eaten as a delicacy. Kew's *Guide to its Museums of Economic Botany*, dated 1886, notes that they "are said to be acrid and poisonous when raw, but innocuous when roasted".

OPPOSITE: *Ginkgo biloba* by Masumi Yamanaka, from *Curtis's Botanical Magazine*, 2013. © Masumi Yamanaka.

ABOVE: Japanese painting of gingko, on board made from the tree and framed by gingko bark: Chikusai Kato at the Koishikawa Botanical Garden, Japan, 1878. Kew Economic Botany Collection.

The Old Lion ginkgo at Kew is actually a male specimen. However, a female graft elicited great excitement when it fruited at Kew in November 1919. This was thought probably to be the first instance of a specimen fruiting in Britain. Kew's Illustrations Collection holds a watercolour sketch dating from 1823 by Thomas Duncanson (below). Almost certainly featuring the ginkgo tree at Kew, the painting clearly shows its male catkins.

The plant has long been used in Chinese medicine to treat a variety of complaints, including respiratory ailments. More recently, Western medicine has sought to examine its potential for treating cardiovascular problems and improving mental agility. Ginkgo's place as a favoured ornamental tree and valuable economic resource will hopefully ensure its longevity for more millennia to come.

BELOW: *Salisburia adiantifolia* (a synonym of *Ginkgo biloba*) by Thomas Duncanson, recording the tree at Kew. Watercolour on paper, 1823.

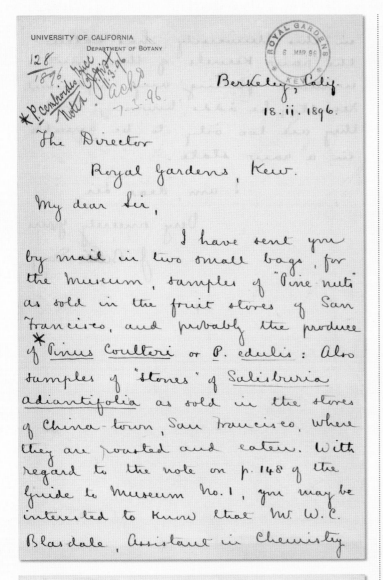

UNIVERSITY OF CALIFORNIA
DEPARTMENT OF BOTANY

*128
1896*

Berkeley, Calif.
18.ii.1896.

The Director
Royal Gardens, Kew.
My dear Sir,

    I have sent you by mail in two small bags, for the museum, samples of "Pine nuts" as sold in the fruit stores of San Francisco, and probably the produce of *Pinus Coulteri* or *P. edulis*: Also samples of "stones" of *Salisburia adiantifolia* as sold in the stores of China-town, San Francisco, where they are roasted and eaten. With regard to the note on p.148 of the Guide to Museum No.1, you may be interested to know that Mr. W.C. Blasdale, Assistant in Chemistry

in this University, has eaten the raw kernels of these fruits without feeling any unpleasant results; he adds, however, that they are too oily to be agreeable in a raw state.

I am, dear Sir,
Very sincerely yours
J. Burtt-Davy

Letter from Joseph Burtt Davy to Sir William Thiselton-Dyer, from University of California, Department of Botany, Berkeley, California, 18 February 1896

Joseph Burtt Davy writes to Kew's Director Sir William Thiselton-Dyer to inform him that he has sent two small bags with samples of pine nuts as sold in the fruit stores of San Francisco, for Kew's museum (now part of Kew's Economic Botany Collection). He thinks they are probably the produce of *Pinus coulteri* or *P. edulis*. He has also sent samples of "stones" of *Salisburia adiantifolia* (ginkgo), as sold in the stores of Chinatown, where they are roasted and eaten.

In addition he writes that in regard to the note on page 148 of *Guide to the Museum No. 1*, Thiselton-Dyer may be interested to know that Mr W. C. Blasdale, Assistant in Chemistry at the University of California, has eaten the raw kernels of these fruits without feeling any unpleasant results, but they are too oily to be agreeable in a raw state.

12 *Ginkgo biloba*, watercolour on Chinese paper, commissioned c.1850 by the botanist and plant hunter Robert Fortune as part of a set of 23 tree portraits.

Tab. 69.

Cucurbita longa, flore albo, protuberante ventre. I.R.H. 107.

Gall. *Calebasse*.— Ital. *Cucuzza a fiasca*

EXPLORING THE SECRETS OF THE BOTTLE GOURD

LAGENARIA SICERARIA

MARK NESBITT

Kew's Economic Botany Collection is a treasure trove of useful plants, but none of its corners is more diverse than the shelves devoted to the bottle gourd, whose dried fruits are used as containers throughout the tropics. Kew's collections include a cricket cage from China, grown inside a mould so as to imprint the surface with Chinese characters, a saké bottle from Japan, ornamented in gold leaf with dancing frogs, snuff bottles from Afghanistan wrapped in silver wire, and musical instruments from Africa and India. There is even a remarkable gourd from New Zealand, engraved with traditional designs by a Maori more than 150 years ago (see overleaf). As well as these precious objects, laden with symbolic value and used to hold valuable materials, there are also larger gourds serving as ladles, cups, fishing floats and water carriers from around the world. Bottle gourds are still used for all these functions, and for food and medicine, today.

The bottle gourd is often confused with the calabash tree (*Crescentia cujete*) and with squashes (several *Cucurbita* species), all of which likewise bear large, fleshy fruits. Bottle gourds, like squashes, are in the Cucurbitaceae family, which also includes melons, cucumbers and watermelon. The plants are annual and are grown from seed; they bear up to 30 fruits, but if large ones are desired it is best to remove all but one. Over time, farmers have selected forms with different-shaped fruits, but shape can also be manipulated, for example, by tying a string around the neck or resting the fruit on the ground to get a flat base. After harvesting, the inside of the mature fruit is soaked so that the pulp and seeds can be removed with a stick.

Kew's specimens mainly date from the 19th century, but the bottle gourd has a much longer history. Today, we think of it as a crop of warmer climes, but the plant first came to Europe as far back as Roman times and was probably grown there. Seeds have been found at Roman sites dating from AD 0–300 and stretching from France to Italy, and waterlogged fragments of its fruits have been recovered from Roman wells. However, the earliest archaeological finds of the bottle gourd come from the Americas, starting 10,000 years ago, and Asia, with finds recorded from China and Japan that date to 9,000 years ago.

The bottle gourd's longstanding distribution across the world has puzzled generations of botanists. Cultivated plants that have a worldwide distribution today are spread either by ocean currents, as

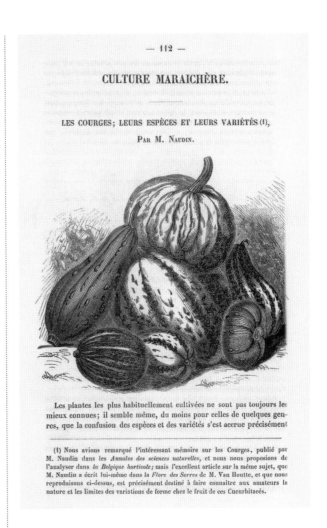

OPPOSITE: *Lagenaria siceraria* (as *Cucurbita longa*), from G. Bonelli: *Hortus Romanus juxta Systema Tournefortianum*, 1783–1816.

ABOVE: *Cucurbita pepo* or summer squash, courgettes, pumpkins etc. from *La Belgique horticole*, 1859.

in the case of coconut fruits that float around the tropics, or by farmers and colonizers. Prehistoric peoples are known to have carried crops over long distances – for example, wheat reached China from the Near East over 4,000 years ago, while canoe-borne travellers carried the sweet potato from South America to Polynesia in about AD 1000. However, it was not clear where the bottle gourd originated, or whether it was spread by oceans or people.

In the last decade, detailed study of the archaeology and botany of the bottle gourd has done much to clarify its history. The wild ancestor of cultivated bottle gourds has recently been found growing in Zimbabwe, pointing to a likely area of origin. These wild gourds have thin fruit rinds (less than 2 mm or $^1/_{12}$ in thick), which break at maturity, allowing the seeds within to be dispersed. In contrast, cultivated gourds have robust fruit rinds, at least 3 mm ($^1/_8$ in) thick. These do not break, thus enabling their use as containers, but at the same time making the gourd dependent on humans for seed dispersal.

All the archaeological records mentioned above are of the thick-walled, cultivated form of gourd. DNA that has been extracted from 8,000-year-old pieces of gourd from the Americas has been found to be closer to that of gourds from Asia than of those from Africa. The combination of early dates and Asian DNA suggests that the bottle gourd was introduced to the Americas by the first people to arrive there – Paleoindians who came from Asia across the Bering Strait. However, the earliest African bottle gourds date to only about 4,000 years ago, raising the question of how the much earlier gourds of Asia arrived there. Overall, however, the picture is clear: the bottle gourd was domesticated by humans before agriculture. The same is true of dogs, which were also taken by Paleoindians into the Americas at an early date. These are perhaps the only plant and animal to have been widely dispersed by humans before the advent of farming.

ABOVE: Bottle gourds incised with Maori designs, given to Kew by William Colenso, 1853. Highly unusually for an inanimate object, the one on the left is decorated with *tā moko* (facial markings). Kew Economic Botany Collection.

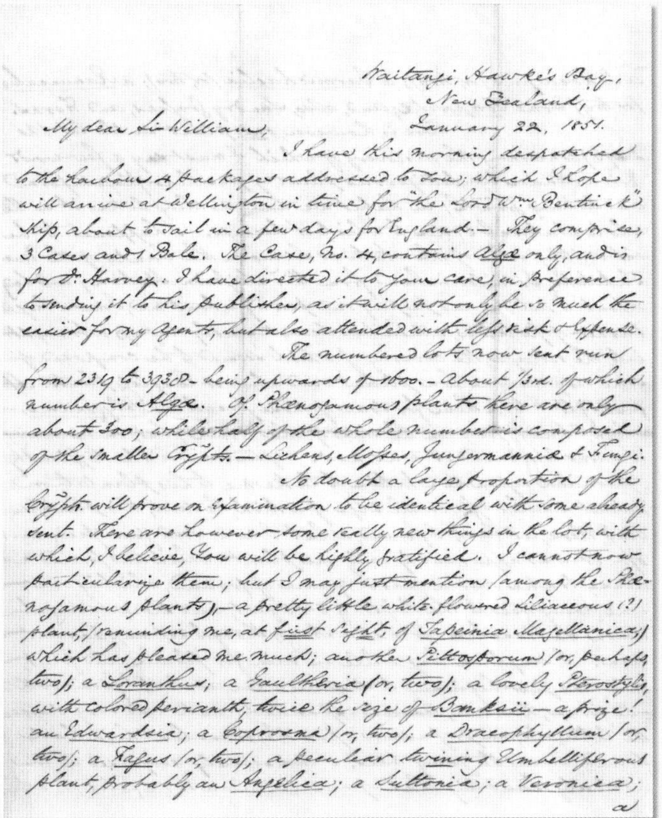

Waitangi, Hawke's Bay,
New Zealand,
January 22, 1851.

My dear Sir William,

I have this morning despatched to the harbour 4 packages addressed to You; which I hope will arrive at Wellington in time for the "Lord Wm. Bentinck" ship, about to sail in a few days for England.— They comprise, 3 Cases and 1 Bale. The Case, No. 4, contains Algæ only, and is for Dr. Harvey: I have directed it to Your care, in preference to sending it to his publisher, as it will not only be so much the easier for my Agents, but also attended with less risk & expense.

The numbered lots now sent run from 2319 to 3930 — being upwards of 1600. — about 1/3rd. of which number is Algæ. Of Phenogamous plants there are only about 300; while half of the whole number is composed of the smaller Crypt. — Lichens, Mosses, Jungermanniæ & Fungi.

No doubt a large proportion of the Crypt. will prove on examination to be identical with some already sent. There are however some really new things in the lot, with which, I believe, You will be highly gratified. I cannot now particularize them; but I may just mention (among the Phenogamous plants), — a pretty little white-flowered Liliaceous (?) plant, (reminding me, at first sight, of Lapageria Magellanica,) which has pleased me much; another Pittosporum (or, perhaps, two); a Loranthus, a Gaultheria (or, two); a lovely Pterostylis, with colored perianth, twice the size of Banksii — a prize! an Edwardsia; a Coprosma (or, two); a Dracophyllum (or, two); a Fagus (or, two); a peculiar twining Umbelliferous plant, probably an Angelica; a Suttonia; a Veronica; a

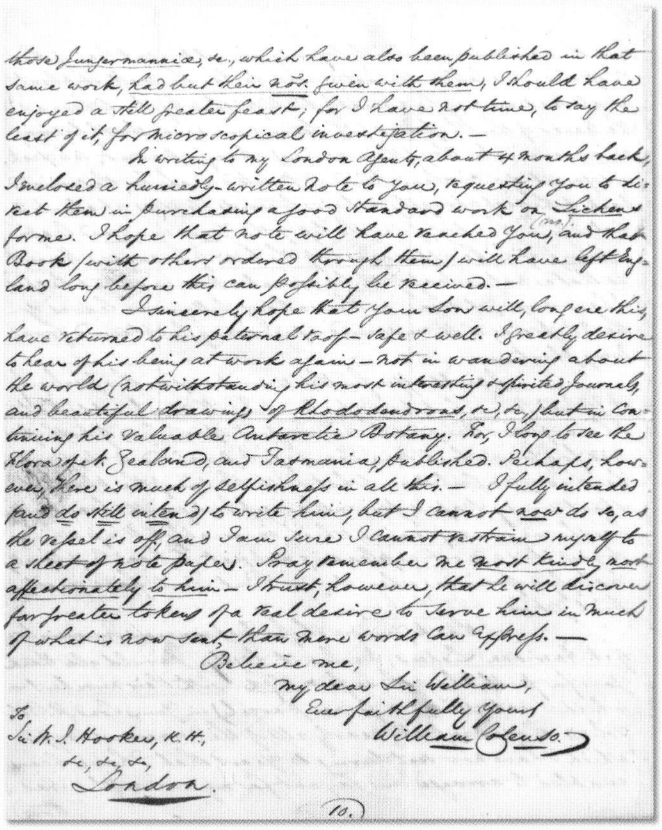

those Jungermanniæ, &c., which have also been published in that same work, had but their [illegible] given with them, I should have enjoyed a still greater feast; for I have not time, to say the least of it, for microscopical investigation. —

In writing to my London Agents, about 4 months back, I enclosed a hurriedly-written note to You, requesting You to direct them in purchasing a good standard work on Lichens for me. I hope that note will have reached You, (ere) and that Book (with others ordered through them) will have left England long before this can possibly be received.—

I sincerely hope that Your Son will, long ere this, have returned to his paternal roof — safe & well. I greatly desire to hear of his being at work again — not in wandering about the world (notwithstanding his most interesting & spirited Journals, and beautiful drawings of Rhododendrons, &c, &c,) but in continuing his valuable Antarctic Botany. For, I long to see the Flora of N. Zealand, and Tasmania, published. Perhaps, however, there is much of selfishness in all this.— I fully intended (and do still intend) to write him, but I cannot now do so, as the vessel is off, and I am sure I cannot restrain myself to a sheet of note paper. Pray remember me most kindly, most affectionately to him — I trust, however, that he will discover far greater tokens of a real desire to serve him in much of what is now sent than mere words can express.—

Believe me,
my dear Sir William,
Ever faithfully Yours
William Colenso.

To
Sir W. J. Hooker, K.H.,
&c, &c, &c,
London.

(10.)

First and last pages of a 10-page letter from William Colenso to Sir William Hooker, from Hawke's Bay, New Zealand, 22 January 1851

This is a covering letter from Colenso to Hooker to accompany samples sent of various local plants and algae, mammals and fabrics. In his lifetime Colenso contributed a number of New Zealand plants and artefacts to Kew's Herbarium and Economic Botany Collection, including the Maori gourd seen opposite.

Colenso was born in Cornwall in 1811 and his early life spent as an apprentice printer led him to obtain the position in his early twenties as printer for the Church Missionary Society in New Zealand. His interest in natural history is said to have been sparked by a visiting Charles Darwin in 1835, when HMS *Beagle* stopped off in the Bay of Islands. Colenso corresponded avidly with William Hooker and also went collecting with his son, Joseph Hooker, who spent four months exploring New Zealand. Colenso collected botanical specimens for the rest of his life, and in total donated over 6,000 specimens to Kew.

13 *Curcurbita lagenaria*, from E. Blackwell: *Herbarium Blackwellianum auctarium, collectio stirpium*, 1750–73.

V. 1.

5

3

B

6

A

4

1

7

8

2

332. *Vitis vinifera L.* **Weinſtock.**

LIFEBLOOD OF THE ANCIENT WORLD
GRAPE VINE

ANNA TRIAS-BLASI

If you were asked to name a plant that has been in cultivation for around 7,000 years, is among the most valuable horticultural crops in the world, has one of the highest levels of beneficial nutrients found in plants and has sweet fruits arranged in a "bunch" … would you guess that it could be the humble grape vine?

The term "grape vine" is used to refer to the species *Vitis vinifera*. This species is further divided into two subspecies: cultivated forms (subsp. *vinifera*) and wild grapes (subsp. *sylvestris*).

The grape vine has a long and rich history, contributing to many ancient civilizations. Drawing on both archaeological and genetic evidence, scientists have suggested that it was domesticated from its wild relative, *V. vinifera* subsp. *sylvestris*, c.4000–3000 BC – around the same time as the invention of the wheel. This occurred in the area between the Caspian and Black seas; the vine was then further domesticated along the Mediterranean basin. *Vitis vinifera* has been prized for its fruit and wine since antiquity, but the wild subspecies and early cultivars of the cultivated subspecies had much smaller fruits, with a much tarter taste, than the grapes we find in shops today.

The grape vine is mentioned in the Bible more than any other plant, and was central to ancient Greek, Etruscan and Roman societies. There are abundant references to *V. vinifera* in Egyptian hieroglyphs, and the earliest complete wine-production facility – dating back about 6,000 years – was discovered in Armenia in 2007. In Greek mythology, the god Dionysus, associated with fertility, is often depicted holding a bunch of grapes or wearing a wreath of vine leaves on his head.

Today, thousands of cultivars are grown. They can be found across each of the Earth's continents with the exception of Antarctica. There, low temperatures and moisture levels, as well as unequal sunlight patterns throughout the year, make for unsuitable growing conditions. Grapes are harvested from approximately 70,000 sq km (27,000 sq miles) of land worldwide, resulting in the production of nearly 70 million tonnes (68.9 million tons) each year. Most of these grapes are turned into wine, but they are also consumed as table grapes, dried as raisins or turned into juice and spirits. Wine can be made from other related species, but *V. vinifera* is the species most commonly used.

Grapes have also been the focus of much biomedical research. The fruit contains abundant phytonutrients thought to aid many of the

OPPOSITE: *Vitis vinifera,* from O. W. Thomé: *Flora von Deutschland, Österreich und der Schweiz*, Tafeln, 1885.

ABOVE: *Vitis vinifera* var. *Chasselas violet* by Pancrace Bessa, from H. L. Duhamel du Monceau: *Traité des arbres et arbustes, Nouvelle édition*, 1819.

LEFT: *Vitis vinifera* var. *Muscat rouge* by Pancrace Bessa, from H. L. Duhamel du Monceau: *Traité des arbres et arbustes, Nouvelle édition*, 1819.

human body's systems: they are known to benefit the respiratory, immune, endocrine and nervous systems, for example. Perhaps most remarkably, they are thought to help prevent cancer, and to regulate cholesterol and blood pressure. And botanists and scientists continue their research to learn more about this important plant and its benefits.

The grape vine was first formally described by Carl Linnaeus as *V. vinifera* in 1753 in his *Species Plantarum* (see opposite).

Left to its own devices, the grape vine can climb very high, often up to 40 m (131 ft), but in cultivation, it is grown to approximately 1–3 m (3–10 ft). Its bark is rough and flaky, and it has tendrils, thread-like structures used by climbing plants to attach themselves to an object or another plant for support. Its leaves are divided into sections originating from a central point, which give it a distinctive shape resembling the fingers of a hand. The flowers are grouped into a branched structure, which then develop into bunches of fruit. The cultivated grape vine is generally hermaphrodite and so able to pollinate itself or other individuals. Its wild relatives have separate male and female plants, however, which need to pollinate each other to reproduce.

The grape vine is certainly the best-known species belonging to the family Vitaceae (also known as the grape family). Yet the Vitaceae family actually comprises around 900 (mostly wild) species, in 14 different genera. New Vitaceae species are discovered every year as botanists continue to document Earth's plant diversity. Vitaceae are mostly climbing vines, distinguished by tendrils that arise from the stem in a position opposite the point of growth of a leaf. Unlike the grape vine, which thrives in warm temperate climates, its relatives mostly prefer areas around the tropics. They can be found in the tropical forests of Asia, Africa, Australia, the Americas and various islands in the Pacific Ocean.

202   PENTANDRIA MONOGYNIA.

cynsbati.   8. RIBES aculeis subaxillaribus, baccis aculeatis racemosis.
Habitat in Canada. *Kalm.* ♂
Facies *præcedentium. Folia parum fissa. Aculeus instar*
spinæ sub alis. Baccæ magnitudine nucis coryli, undi-
que armatæ aculeis robustis.

GRONOVIA.

scandens.   1. GRONOVIA. *Hort. cliff.* 74.
Gronovia scandens lappacea, pampinea fronde. *Housl.*
Mart. cent. 1. p. 40. t. 40. *Amm. herb.* 346.
Habitat in Vera Cruce.

HEDERA.

Helix.   1. HEDERA foliis ovatis lobatisque. *Fl. lapp.* 91. Fl.
suec. 190. *Hort. cliff.* 74. *Mat. med.* 98. *Roy. lugdb.*
223. *Hall. helv.* 164.
Hedera arborea. *Bauh. pin.* 305.
β·Hedera poëtica. *Bauh. pin.* 305.
γ·Hedera major sterilis. *Bauh. pin.* 305.
Habitat in Europæ *arboribus putrescentibus, inque sepi-*
bus. ♂

quinquefolia 2. HEDERA foliis quinatis ovatis serratis. *Hort. cliff.*
74. *Roy. lugdb.* 223. *Gron. virg.* 24.
Vitis hederacea indica. *Stapel. theatr.* 364.
Edera quinquefolia canadensis. *Corn. canad.* 99. *t.* 100.
Helix. *Mitch. gen.* 30.
Habitat in Canada. ♂
Capsula *utrinque turbinata, bilocularis, polysperma.* Flo-
res *masculi a feminis distincti* D. Mitchell.

VITIS.

vinifera.   1. VITIS foliis lobatis sinuatis nudis.
Vitis foliis palmato-angulatis. *Hort. cliff.* 74. *Hort.*
upf. 50. *Mat. med.* 97. *Gron. virg.* 144. *Roy. lugdb.*
222.
Vitis vinifera. *Bauh. pin.* 229.
apyrena.   β. Vitis corinthiaca f. apyrena. *Bauh. hist.* 2. p. 72.
Habitat in Orbis quatuor partibus temperatis. ♂

indica.   2. VITIS foliis cordatis dentatis subtus villosis, cirrhis ra-
cemiferis. *Fl. zeyl.* 99. *
Vitis sylvestris indica, acinis rotundis, *Raj. dendr.* 67
Habitat in India. ♂

3. VI-

PENTANDRIA MONOGYNIA.   203

Labrusca,   3. VITIS foliis cordatis subtrilobis dentatis subtus tomen-
tosis.
Vitis sylvestris virginiana. *Bauh. pin.* 299.
Vitis vinifera sylvestris americana, foliis aversa parte den-
sa lanugine tectis. *Pluk. phyt.* 249. f. 1.
Vitis fructu minore rubro acerbo, folio subrotundo minus laciniato, subtus alba lanugine tecto, *Sloan. hist.*
2. p. 104. t. 210. f. 4.
Habitat in America septentrionali. ♂

vulpina,   4. VITIS foliis cordatis dentato-serratis utrinque nudis.
Vitis vulpina dicta virginiana nigra. *Pluk. alm.* 392.
Vitis aceris folio. *Raj. dendr.* 68.
Habitat in Virginia. ♂

trifolia,   5. VITIS foliis ternatis: foliolis subrotundis serratis.
Vitis pearine doorica, foliis ternis subrotundis serratis.
Raj. dendr. 68.
Habitat in India. ♂

laciniosa,   6. VITIS foliis quinatis: foliolis multifidis. *Hort. cliff.*
74. *Roy. lugdb.* 223.
Vitis laciniatis foliis. *Corn. canad.* 182. t. 183.
Vitis apii folio. *Bauh. hist.* 2. p. 73.
Habitat - - - - ♂

arborea,   7. VITIS foliis supradecompositis: foliolis lateralibus pinnatis.
Vitis caroliniana, foliis apii, uva corymbosa purpurascen-
te. *Act. bonon.* 2. part. 2. p. 365. t. 24.
Frutex scandens, petroselini foliis, virginianus claviculis
donatus, *Pluk. mant.* 85. t. 412
Habitat in Carolina, Virginica. ♂

LAGOECIA.

Cuminoides.   1. LAGOECIA. *Hort. cliff.* 73. *Hort. upf.* 52.
Cuminum sylvestre, capitulis globosis. *Bauh. pin.* 186.
Cuminum sylvestre. *Cam. epit.* 518.
Habitat in Creta, Lemno, Lysia, Galatia. ☉

SAUVAGESIA.

erecta,   1. SAUVAGESIA.
Habitat in Domingo.
Habitas Hyperici aut Corchori. Caulis erectus. Folia
alterna, ovato-lanceolata, obtuse serrata. Stipulæ acutæ,
ciliatæ.

CLA-

Title page and extract from *Species Plantarum* by Carl Linnaeus, 1753

Description of *Vitis vinifera* in *Species Plantarum*, the seminal work of botanist Carl Linnaeus (1707–78). First published in 1753 in Stockholm, it showed for the first time Linnaeus's remarkable system of binomial plant names in use, describing over 7,300 species. Instead of long and complex titles, in which many words were strung together, Linnaeus combined a single-word genus name with a specific descriptive word (or "trivial name") for each species. This marked the beginning of our modern method of naming plants.

Linnaeus read medicine and botany at Uppsala University and also studied in the Netherlands. In 1736 he visited England, meeting Sir Hans Sloane and Philip Miller, keeper of the Chelsea Physic Garden, whom he impressed with his new method of subdividing plants. Linnaeus helped to found the Royal Swedish Academy of Science in Stockholm and in 1741 was appointed Professor of Medicine at Uppsala. Later he became responsible for the botanical garden, botany and natural history, encouraging his students to collect botanical samples.

After his death, Linnaeus's collection, including 14,000 plants, 3,198 insects and 1,600 books, was bought by a 24-year-old medical student, James Edward Smith, who founded the Linnean Society of London in 1788.

14   *Vitis vinifera var. Bourdelas noir* by Pancrace Bessa, from H. L. Duhamel du Monceau: *Traité des arbres et arbustes*, Nouvelle édition, 1819.

THE HEAVY PRICE OF SUGAR CANE
SACCHARUM OFFICINARUM

MARK NESBITT AND MARIA VORONTSOVA

It is hard now to imagine a time when sweet substances were hard to come by. Yet very few natural substances can be used as sweeteners. Those that do exist, such as honey, some fruits and plant saps like maple syrup, have all been scarce and expensive in past centuries. The arrival of the sugar cane in the New World, inextricably linked with slavery, was radically to change this.

Sugar cane is a beautiful erect plant. It usually grows to between 2 and 4 m (6ft 6 in–13 ft) tall, and has a strong stem superficially resembling bamboo. Both sugar cane and bamboo belong to the botanical family Poaceae, the grasses, but they originated from different evolutionary lineages. Bamboos are related to rice and to the temperate grasses, while sugar cane is a member of a tropical grass tribe called the Andropogoneae. Sugar cane flowers are hidden inside several layers of modified, leaf-like bracts. A group of two flowers and several bracts arranged together is called a spikelet, and every spikelet is surrounded by long, fine, silver hairs. These have evolved to disperse sugar cane seeds with gusts of wind, similar to the dispersal of dandelion seeds. The spikelets surrounded by silver hairs are arranged in numerous long branches, forming a generous white, fluffy inflorescence.

Sugar cane is a close relative of *Miscanthus*, a commonly planted, decorative grass cultivated for its own attractive inflorescences, also white and fluffy, with a very similar structure. Like sugar cane, the plant is used as a biofuel due to its rapid growth. Both sugar cane and *Miscanthus* use a modified system of photosynthesis called C4, enabling more efficient sugar production in hot, dry climates.

In recent history, sugar cane has strong associations with the Caribbean and Brazil, where today it is a major source of ethanol for biofuel production. Its origins lie deep in Southeast Asia, however, in the island of New Guinea, where the wild grass *Saccharum robustum* was first taken into cultivation, perhaps 8,000 years ago. Sugar cane was taken to India, where it crossed naturally with another grass, leading to the sweet forms from which sugar could be extracted. Ancient Sanskrit texts show that the Indian sugar industry dates back 4,000 years. They describe the production of many different kinds of sugar, including *khanda*, recorded in a text of 300 BC and the source of the word "candy". The knowledge of how to press sugar cane in a mechanical mill, and how to crystallize the juice, travelled eastward to

OPPOSITE: *Saccharum officinarum* from F. P. Chaumeton: *Flore médicale*, 1832.

ABOVE: Crude sugar, collected in Mozambique by Dr Livingstone's Zambesi Expedition, 1860. Kew Economic Botany Collection.

China by AD 200. It also spread westward, reaching the Mediterranean by AD 700. Sugar cane cultivation entered areas such as the Nile valley, the Levant, Cyprus, Spain and Morocco in the wake of the Arab conquests, and flourished under Crusader occupation of the Levant in the 12th and 13th centuries. However, by 1600, Brazilian sugar dominated European markets, produced at a far lower price thanks to the country's climate and slavery.

In the 18th century, sugar production became more widespread in tropical America, entirely dominating the economy of islands such as Hispaniola, Jamaica and Cuba. Money acquired in the sugar trade supported planters and generated great wealth among importers; it thus played an important role in driving wider trade. Institutions such as the British Museum were founded on fortunes made from sugar. The idealized life shown in contemporary landscape paintings, in which sugar plantations were transformed into arcadian landscapes,

was of course a fantasy. In reality, the heavy labour demands of sugar cultivation, especially cutting the cane and boiling the juice, were fed by the enslaved, imported from West Africa. After slavery was outlawed in the 19th century, British planters turned to indentured labour – a highly exploitative system of forced labour for Chinese and Indian immigrants that was at times little better than slavery.

Sugar cane has left a troubled legacy for modern times. Cane-sugar prices have fallen steeply, damaging the economy of producing countries, especially in the Caribbean and Central America, and sugar beet now accounts for 30 per cent of world production. On a more positive note, 40 per cent of sugar sold in British supermarkets is Fairtrade cane sugar, guaranteeing fair payments to farmers. At the same time, sugar is under attack for its role in obesity and related illnesses, such as forms of diabetes. Perhaps, in the future, sugar will once again be treated as a rare treat in our kitchens.

LEFT: *Harvesting the sugar cane in Minas Geraes, Brazil*, by Marianne North, 1872–73.

CHAPTER III

JAMAICA

In the West Indies at last! Christmas Eve!

We passed Watling's Island and Rum Key, and after steaming through the crooked island passage we had a most exquisite sunset, the gold melting into pure blue so suddenly, and yet so softly, that one could hardly say where the beginning or ending of either colour was. What a contrast in one week! All the blankets were taken out of the cabin, and one sheet was almost unendurable, with both door and windows open. The next day we were within sight of Cuba, and the sunset had all the soft colours of a wood-pigeon's breast. I gave up the greater part of my dinner to enjoy it. The clouds closed in over it, till at last there was but one opening like a golden eye with red eyelashes, all the rest different shades of neutral tint, the land under it very green, while the sea looked like ink. The approach to Port Royal, with its long spit of sand and mangrove swamp, and then into the calm bay of Kingston beyond, was intensely exciting. Every tree was of a new form to me, the grand mountains rising gradually up to 7000 or 8000 feet beyond, all creased and crumpled with ins and outs, like brown paper which has been much used.

Extract from *Recollections of a Happy Life* by Marianne North, 1892

First page of chapter 3 from the published memoirs of Victorian artist Marianne North. A remarkable Victorian traveller and painter, Marianne traversed the globe, recording the world's flora in her stunning paintings and writing her experiences in her journal, which later became the basis for her autobiography.

In this extract from her autobiography, Marianne is in Jamaica, where she has arrived on Christmas Eve 1871. During her time there, she wrote about and painted many economic plants, including sugar cane. She describes a visit to a sugar plantation: "The sugar-canes grew here magnificently, planted sufficiently wide apart to allow a plough to be worked between the rows. They threw up from fifty to eighty canes in one bunch, and were often fourteen feet high. Rats are their chief enemies, gnawing the cane near the ground so that it falls and dies. A penny was offered for every dead rat, and often 1,000 were killed in one week."

Throughout *The Botanical Treasury* there are many examples of Marianne's work, all of which are housed in the Marianne North Gallery at Kew, built in 1879 at her own expense. The gallery houses each of the artist's 833 paintings, which between them depict more than 900 species of plants.

15 *Saccharum officinarum,* from F. E. Köhler: *Medizinal Pflanzen,* 1890.

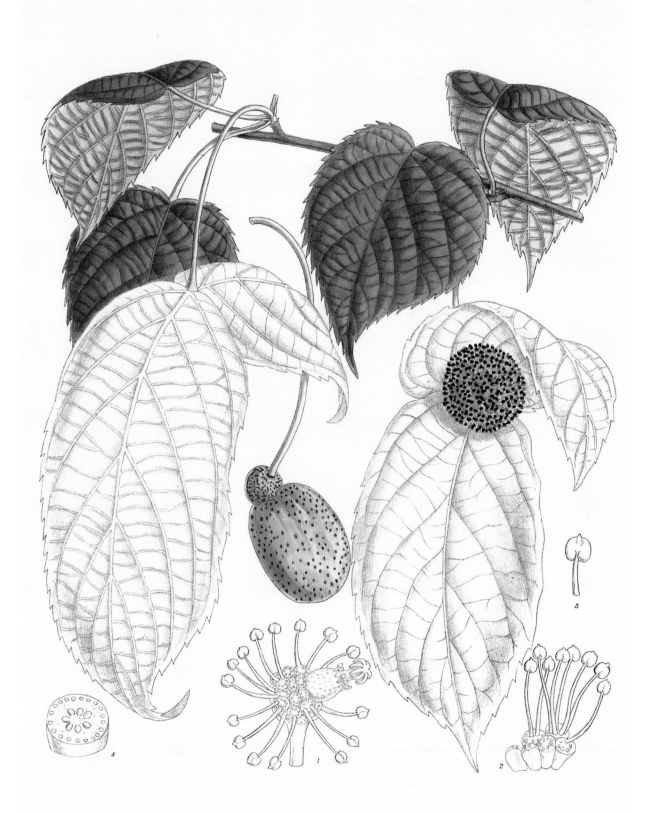

DELICATE DANCERS FROM THE EAST
HANDKERCHIEF TREE

MARTYN RIX

When in full flower, the *Davidia* is one of the most striking of all trees; its common names, dove tree and handkerchief tree, describe the white flowers which hang on long slender stalks all along under the branches, twisting and pirouetting in the slightest breeze.

The name *Davidia* commemorates one of the pioneering French missionary–naturalists, many of whom went to the lawless mountains of western China in the latter part of the 19th century. Père Armand David was a Catholic priest, a Basque from Espelette (or Ezpeleta) in the foothills of the Pyrenees near Biarritz. He trained as a science teacher and taught in schools in northern Italy and Istanbul before persuading his superiors to send him to China, as much as a scientist as a missionary. His first collecting expedition, from Beijing into Inner Mongolia, concentrated on geology and ornithology; it was in the Emperor's hunting park at Nan Haizi near Beijing where he saw the deer that was also to be named after him, *Elaphurus davidianus*.

It was not until 1869, when he was 43, that David reached the isolated mountain kingdom of Mupin, now called Baoxing – a deep, narrow valley in the borderland between China and Tibet, with dense forest leading up into snow-capped mountains on three sides. Here, even more exciting animals, birds and plants were waiting to be collected and described: the giant panda, rare pheasants and the strange large tree that stood out from the rest of the forest because of its white, fluttering flowers.

As the first scientist to collect in this wonderfully rich area, David is reported to have collected 63 new species of animal, 65 new species of bird and hundreds of new plants, including 52 rhododendrons. *Clematis armandii* and *Acer davidii* are two familiar garden plants named after him. David also wrote a detailed journal in which he describes the almost incessant rain and the local hunters who helped him collect animals and plants. The church and seminary where he stayed has now been restored, and young *Davidia* trees have been planted round the courtyard where it stands.

David did not send seed of his tree back to Europe, probably because it was not then ripe. The first collections were made by another missionary, Père Farges, who sent a few seeds back to France in 1897,

OPPOSITE: *Davidia involucrata* var. *vilmoriniana* by Matilda Smith, from *Curtis's Botanical Magazine*, 1912.

ABOVE: Père Armand David.

and by Ernest Wilson, who travelled across China in 1903 and 1904 especially to find it. He managed to track down trees further east near the Ichang (Yichang) gorges of the Yangtze River, site of the famous modern giant dam, and sent back such quantities that his employer, Veitch's Nurseries at Coombe Wood in Surrey, was able to raise 13,000 young plants between 1905 and 1910.

A few of these original trees have survived, usually in damp, sheltered gardens as the tree is susceptible to drought; indeed it thrives in boggy conditions, which suit its shallow roots. Young trees do not normally flower for the first ten years or so, but after that they flower freely. The actual flowers are a dense tuft of stamens and a single ovary, hidden at the base of the two white bracts. Each flower sets one green fruit that has a hard, ridged seed inside; this contains up to five embryos, each of which can grow into a new tree. The leaves are delicately ribbed and the side branches almost horizontal, so even a young tree is an elegant addition to any garden.

ABOVE: Ernest Henry "Chinese" Wilson, from *The Gardeners' Chronicle*, 1905.

LEFT: Kew Herbarium specimen of *Davidia involucrata* collected in China by Augustine Henry, 1889.

Memorandum

Cercis racemosa, oliver (Hk. Ic Pl. t. 1894), [Henry, China no. 5602] was found by me only in one spot, namely Ma-huang-p'o, in South Wushan district, i.e. South of Pei-shih about 30 miles. Pei-shih is a village on the Yangtze, just on the Szechwan–Hupeh frontier: and Ma-huang-p'o, which is very elevated, perhaps 6000 feet, can be approached from Pei-shih by a road, such as the salt-carriers go by. — The road runs practically east along the Szechwan–Hupeh frontier South of the Yangtze.

The other species of Cercis which is common in the mountains,

namely, Cercis chinensis, Bge is called the Lo-chün (LO-CHÜN) or Lo-chiang tree (de Henry, Names of Chinese Plants, nos. 252, 391, 509): and any native sent to collect pods of Cercis racemosa must be advised, that it is the small Lo-chün tree of Ma-huang-p'o, which is wanted, and not the common species.

I can only suggest that some resident of Ichang, e.g. the Consul or one of the missionaries be addressed on the subject: and that a drawing of the tree, copied from the Ic. Pl. be sent. This may seem hardly worth while, considering the risk of failure: but in the present case, there is an

opportunity of killing two birds with one stone. In the same locality occurs the wonderfully strange and beautiful tree, Davidia involucrata: and fruit of it for introduction would be worth while taking an immensity of trouble.

Mr. Ford once sent a man from Hongkong to Ichang for lily bulbs: and as he is now in England, perhaps you had better consult him. At Ichang it will be very still, through the Catholic missionaries to get some of the coolies who went with me on my big trip.

In conclusion I would suggest that drawings of both

Cercis racemosa & of Davidia involucrata be sent to Ichang to someone there: and an effort be made to get ripe fruits of both species. Perhaps October would be the best month for the coolie to go up from Ichang: and if on his return the seeds were found immature, he could make another trip immediately. It should be insisted on that the coolie bring back with him branches bearing fruit & leaves of both trees, so that no mistake may be made in the matter.

Aug. Henry

Mengtze, 8 June, 1897.

Memorandum from Augustine Henry to Sir William Thiselton-Dyer, from Mengtze (Wenlan, China), 8 June 1897

Henry's memorandum refers to *Cercis racemose*, which he has found in only one location, Ma-huang-p'o in south Wushan (Wuhan) district, south of Pei-shih, a small village on the Yangtze River on the Hupeh–Szechwan (Hubei–Sichuan) border. The other species of *Cercis* common in the mountains is *Cercis chinensis*, known as the *lo-chün* or *lo-chiang* tree.

In the same locality occurs the "wonderfully strange and beautiful" *Davidia involucrata*, which he advises is worth introducing for the fruit. Mr Ford once sent a man to Ichang for lily bulbs; he is now in England and might be consulted. It might be possible to get some of the "coolies" who accompanied Henry originally, through the Catholic missionaries. He suggests sending drawings of both plants to someone in Ichang, and making an effort to get ripe fruit of both species as well as branches bearing fruit and leaves.

16 *Davidia involucrata* by Masumi Yamanaka, from M. Yamanaka, C. Harrison and M. Rix: *Treasured Trees*, 2015. © Masumi Yamanaka.

EVERYWHERE OVER THE RAINBOW

IRIS

TONY HALL

Iris was named for the Greek goddess of the rainbow, and irises come in a variety of colours – a major attraction for gardeners. With more than 290 accepted *Iris* species, according to the World Checklist of Selected Plant Families, this is the largest genus within the Iridaceae family, and a handful of more recently published species names are waiting to be added to the list. Irises extend across much of the temperate Northern Hemisphere, enjoying habitats as diverse as rocky alpine slopes, steppe and semi-desert, woodland and waterside; at least one species, *Iris halophila*, is even tolerant of salt water. They range from 6 cm (2¼ in) to well over 1 m (3 ft) tall in bloom, with flowers that are often highly scented and extraordinarily variable in form and size. The underground parts may be rhizomatous or bulbous. In the largest natural group of irises, the Junos – primarily dryland plants from Western and Central Asia – species have both a bulb and persistent fleshy to swollen storage roots; sometimes they even possess a third storage organ – a pseudo-bulb – formed from the base of the previous season's flower stem.

Irises have a long history of medicinal and cosmetic use. The ancient Egyptians used dried iris roots as a fragrance. In the 1st century AD, the physician and herbalist Dioscorides advocated the use of iris rhizomes in treatments for sleeplessness, ulcers, freckles, gynaecological problems and other conditions. The Japanese grew their native *I. laevigata* for use as a vegetable dye in the Nara Period (AD 710–794) and bred selected garden forms certainly from the early to mid-Edo Period of the early 17th century; although there are no written records, it is likely that they were developing decorative varieties of the even more popular *I. ensata* long before that. Today, the Chinese still use their native irises in herbal remedies, for example *I. anguifuga* is used both as a laxative and to treat snake bites. In Italy, the scented rhizomes of the bearded *I.* x *florentina*, or orris root, were once used medicinally and still contribute to the perfume and cosmetics industry; "orris" is simply a corruption of one of the Italian words for iris, *ireos*. In parts of Central Asia, *I. lactea* is used as cattle fodder where other plants will not grow, while fibres from its tough foliage have been exploited to make string and coarse cloth. And bearded irises have long been planted around Muslim graveyards in places such as the Middle East.

OPPOSITE: *Iris variegata* by Georg Dionysius Ehret, 1764.

ABOVE: *Iris dykesii* by Lilian Snelling, 1927.

It is primarily the beauty and variability of its flower, however, that has ensured the iris's popularity as a garden plant. Societies in North America, Australia, New Zealand, Italy and Japan are devoted to the study, cultivation and breeding of irises. The genus is extremely diverse in the form of its underground parts, growth habit, foliage and flower characteristics, and many systematic arrangements have been proposed, including recent attempts to confine genus *Iris* to the rhizomatous bearded species only. However, such an extreme approach is not generally accepted. Where they have been studied and cultivated for centuries, certain *Iris* species have a complex nomenclatural history. For example, the Mediterranean *I. planifolia*, which was known to the horticulturalist Clusius in the 16th century, can boast 23 synonyms or alternative botanical names.

ABOVE: *Iris planifolia* (as *Iris bulbosa latifolia*), from C. van de Passe: *Hortus floridus*, 1614.

RIGHT: *Iris sysirunchium* by Georg Dionysius Ehret, 1770.

Extract from *De Materia Medica* by Dioscorides Pendanius
of Anazarbos, 1529 translation of AD 50–70 original

This description of *Iris* is taken from a Latin translation of *De Materia Medica* published in Cologne in 1529. The Greek original, written in AD 50–70 by Dioscorides, a Roman doctor of Greek descent, was one of the few works of antiquity known in medieval times, through hand-copied manuscripts, often including commentaries from Arabic or Indian sources. Early Greek manuscripts, some lavishly illustrated, still survive, as do densely illustrated copies in Arabic from the 12th and 13th centuries. Printed editions appear from the Renaissance onwards, translated into Italian, Spanish, German and French. An English translation was made by John Goodyer in 1655.

Today the *De Materia Medica* is our best source of details about the medicines used in ancient Greece and Rome. The five-volume work covers around 600 plants and 1,000 medicines derived from them. An early pharmacopoeia, it primarily covers medical uses, but also refers to culinary uses and identification techniques. Dioscorides's descriptions are not easy to follow, partly because he describes plants of southeast Europe whereas his book was later read across Europe and the Islamic world. Herbals in England continued to classify plants by smell, taste, medical uses and whether they were edible or not, well into the 16th and 17th centuries.

17 *Iris bulbosa* by Georg Dionysius Ehret, 1757.

Lilium canadense
Willu. sp. pl. 2 p 89
Ait. hort. kew. ed. alt. 2 p 240

THE SEARCH FOR THE SIROI LILY
LILIUM MACKLINIAE

LORNA CAHILL

On 5 June 1948, newlyweds Mr and Mrs Kingdon-Ward climbed for six hours up the Siroi hill range of Manipur, India. They were seeking specimens of a new species of lily which Frank Kingdon-Ward had first seen two years before. He was determined to send bulbs to the New York Botanic Garden, which was funding this expedition. However, the peak time of the Siroi lily's bloom was coming to an end and he could not hire enough local people to help him set up camp at the high altitude where the lily grew. On the verge of giving up, Frank suggested that if they could not camp in the Siroi hills, the couple could still trek the 40 km (25 miles) from their base in Ukhrul to the peak and back in a day, hopefully finding the lilies in the few hours available before they would need to descend the mountain again. His wife Jean readily agreed.

Francis "Frank" Kingdon-Ward had been exploring Asia and collecting plants for nurseries since 1911, after giving up a teaching career in China. He soon began to make his name after collecting the first viable seed of the Himalayan blue poppy *Meconopsis betonicifolia*. In 1913, he published an account of this expedition – *The Land of the Blue Poppy: Travels of a naturalist in eastern Tibet* – and also wrote articles and delivered lectures on the subject in the UK. His long and successful career in exploration and plant collecting included several expeditions through India, Burma (Myanmar) and China.

Kingdon-Ward's diaries, held in Kew's Archives, show that he did much more than collect plants. He recorded observations of the places through which he travelled, describing the local people he encountered, the terrain and vegetation, wildlife and weather. His careful attention to detail and often poetic language make the diaries incredibly rich and a pleasure to read: "The banks were coated with moss like green jade ... Birds were calling gaily. We saw the sun rise over the Sirhoi range like an incandescent aluminium or very pale copper disc."

During the Second World War, Kingdon-Ward was recruited by the Special Operations Executive (SOE). His experience of travelling across Asia was useful in providing survival training to pilots at the School of Jungle Warfare in India. It was after the war, during a mission to locate fallen aircraft in the jungle between India and China, that he first found the Siroi lily. Two years later, now in his sixties, he was finally able to continue his plant collecting and his hunt for the lily,

OPPOSITE: *Lilium canadense* from M. Catesby: *The Natural History of Carolina, Florida, and the Bahama Islands*, 1754.

RIGHT: *Nerine sarniensis* (as *Amaryllis sarniensis*) by Pierre Joseph Redouté, from P. J. Redouté: *Les Liliacées*, 1805–16.

LEFT: *Lilium mackliniae* by Stella Ross-Craig, from *Curtis's Botanical Magazine*, 1950.

and this time, he had his young wife Jean, aged 26, to accompany him.

Sixteen km (ten miles) into their journey to Siroi, the couple began to see lilies in bloom – happily in their hundreds. Soon Jean spotted a perfect specimen, 1.5 m (5 ft) high with fully open satiny-white and rose-pink flowers and a deep crimson nectary. Frank photographed it and Jean carefully placed it in a press for drying. They made several other discoveries and collections, but soon had to begin their return journey, reaching home 14 hours after starting out. "It was by far the longest, and most successful day we have had yet," noted Frank in his diary.

The new lily was successfully cultivated back in the UK, and was formally described by J. Robert Sealy in 1949. He gave it the name *Lilium mackliniae* at Kingdon-Ward's request – named for Jean, whose maiden name was Macklin. It can be successfully grown in a temperate climate, as it is hardy and long-lived.

In his account of the Manipur expedition, published in 1952, Kingdon-Ward devoted a whole chapter to the "Glorious Fifth of June". The book also includes the dedication "For Jean, who enjoyed every day of it".

Ukhrul.
20th May, 1948.

Darlingest Frank,

Is it very silly to write to someone who's only in the next room? and when there's nothing to say except to thank you so very much, sweet-heart, for a lovely three weeks plant-hunting, and to utter the cliché of all clichés — that I love you with all my heart for ever & ever, oh, so much, darling; if I could only tell you how much.

Must stop now, as there's lots to do.
God bless you, sweet,
All my love always,
from your Jean

Letter from Jean Kingdon-Ward to Frank, 20 May 1948

Frank and Jean Kingdon-Ward made six expeditions together. His diaries and published written accounts show that Frank greatly appreciated his wife's positive outlook, practical help with collecting and fortitude during the difficult aspects of their travels. This touching letter from Kew's Archives also reveals Jean's feelings:

"Darlingest Frank,

Is it very silly to write to someone who's only in the next room? And when there's nothing to say except thank you so very much, sweet-heart, for a lovely three weeks plant-hunting…

All my love always,

From your Jean."

18 *Lilium orientalis*
by Margaret
Meen, c.1780s.

THE LOTUS:
A SACRED SYMBOL OF THE EAST
NELUMBO

JULIA BUCKLEY

The name "lotus" has been loosely applied to a number of plants, including various species of waterlilies that rather resemble the true lotus and enjoy a similar aquatic habitat. In fact, lotus refers to two specific species of *Nelumbo* – *Nelumbo nucifera* and *Nelumbo lutea* – placed within the family Nelumbonaceae. The ancient plant is closer genetically to the Platanaceae and Proteaceae families, to which plane trees and proteas belong. *Nelumbo nucifera* is white to pink and distributed in Asia and northeast Australia, while *N. lutea* is yellow in colour and native to North America. Lotuses have large flowers that can be approximately 20 cm (8 in) in diameter, at the centre of which the characteristic flat-topped seed pod will develop. The petiole, or leaf stalk, attaches to the centre of their large shield-shaped leaves, which often stand proud above the water. Nelumbos are pollinated by small insects and grow in shallow reserves of water, reaching out their rhizomes from the muddy bed beneath.

Fossilized impressions of lotus leaves and rhizomes have been dated back millions of years. In 1995, the plant was successfully germinated from seeds around 1,290 years old, found on a dry lake bed in northeastern China. In *The Odyssey,* Homer describes how Odysseus encounters a tribe of "Lotus-Eaters" on his return from Troy. His men consume the plant and descend into a state of blissful forgetfulness. The ancient Greeks used the misnomer *lōtos* to describe several plants; in his *Illustrations of the Lotus of the Ancients, and Tamara of India* (1816), Richard Duppa surmises that Homer's plant may have been *Ziziphus lotus,* an unrelated member of the buckthorn family fermented for alcohol. The phrase "to eat lotus" was adopted by ancient writers as a metaphor meaning "to forget". Lord Tennyson revisited the theme in his poem of 1832, "The Lotos-Eaters".

Lotus has long been regarded as a sacred plant. *N. nucifera* has great symbolic significance within both Hindu and Buddhist traditions, as noted by William Roxburgh, Superintendent of Calcutta Botanic Garden. He wrote that: "These holy and beautiful plants are often met with in ... religious ceremonies ... under their Sanscrit name Padma." Artists working for Roxburgh in the Calcutta Botanic Garden produced several illustrations of the lotus, later used to inform descriptions in *Flora Indica* (1820–32), a written record of the plants Roxburgh encountered in India, and carvings of the lotus feature widely in Eastern art, decorating deities and the pillars of temples. Its spiritual associations may stem from connotations of purity: the lotus can self-cleanse by repelling water, and so remain clean and untainted by its surroundings. Scientific research is seeking to replicate the "lotus effect" technique in modern technology.

The lotus is also exploited for its medicinal, edible and material properties. Kew's Economic Botany Collection holds prayer beads and flour made from lotus seeds. In China and Japan, its rhizomes are a staple food, and lotus leaves, flowers and stalks are also consumed in India.

Nelumbo nucifera was introduced to Kew by Sir Joseph Banks in 1784, and features in various letters held in Kew's Archives. In 1876, Sir Joseph Hooker sent a quantity of lotus to the Water Lily Gardens at Bordentown, New Jersey from where the nurseryman Edmund D. Sturtevant wrote to William Watson, Assistant Curator at Kew, in 1889, to describe the "sensation" caused in the gardens after their introduction there. Sturtevant was astounded by the scale of the plant. In an article of the same year for *Garden & Forest,* he revealed: "The tallest man is hidden from view when walking through the mass of foliage."

Robert Thornton featured the lotus in his celebrated botanical work *The Temple of Flora* (1799–1807), where he entitled it "The Sacred Egyptian Bean". He commissioned the artist Peter Henderson to illustrate both forms of the *Nelumbo* set against a background of distant pyramids. Thornton notes that the lotus can no longer be found in Egypt, a fact attested to by the 19th-century botanical artist Marianne North. It was, she wrote, "the emblem of sanctity in Egypt amongst the priests of a religion long ago extinct; and the plant itself has long been extinct in that country".

OPPOSITE: *Nelumbo nucifera* (as *Nymphaea nelumbo*) by R. J. Thornton: *New Illustration of the Sexual System of Carolus von Linnaeus and the Temple of Flora, or Garden of Nature,* 1807.

LEFT: Lotus, artist unknown (China).

BELOW: *Nelumbo speciosum* in the Water Lily Gardens at Bordentown, New Jersey, USA, 1889.

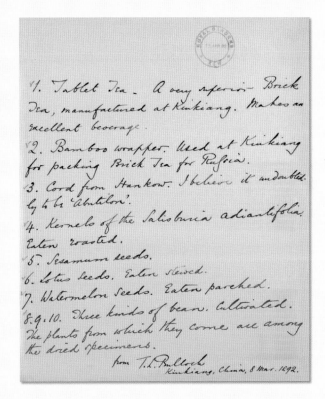

First page of letter and list from Thomas Lowden Bullock to the Royal Botanic Gardens,
Kew, from HBM Consulate, Kinkiang (Kin Kiang), China, 8 March 1892

In this letter, Thomas Lowden Bullock explains that he is sending Kew a parcel, containing a small packet of dried plants he collected in China last autumn and which he would be glad to have identified as far as possible. The parcel also contains a few packets of seed, which he thought the gardeners might like to try, and a few botanical products for the museum. He hopes some of these last items may be useful. Bullock notes it is not easy to find dry products about which one can be sure as to the plant from which they came. He encloses a list of the products. If he can make himself useful to Kew he asks to be notified. The accompanying list details the products Bullock has sent, comprising: tablet tea, a superior Brick tea manufactured at Kinkiang; a bamboo wrapper used at Kinkiang for packing Brick tea for Russia; cord from Hankow (Hankou); kernels of the *Salisburia adiantifolia* which are eaten roasted; sesamum seeds; lotus seeds that are eaten stewed; watermelon seeds which are eaten parched; and three kinds of cultivated bean. The plants, from which the latter came, are amongst the dried specimens.

19 *Nelumbium speciosum*, from the Roxburgh Collection, Kew, late 18th/early 19th century.

A PRIMITIVE PIONEER
MAGNOLIA

CHRIS CLENNETT

Mark Catesby was one of the first plant collectors to explore what is now the eastern United States. He brought seed of *Magnolia grandiflora* back to Britain in 1726, more than 50 years before the USA was founded. This made it only the second magnolia species to be introduced to European cultivation from America; the first was *M. virginiana*, a smaller deciduous species collected a few years earlier. The latter species was certainly being grown at Fulham Palace by Dr Compton in 1688. The introduction must have astonished plant lovers in Britain – here was an evergreen magnolia that looked impressive throughout the year and bore enormous flowers in summer.

How the plant acquired the common name of bull bay is unknown, although some people believed that plants with long, evergreen, elliptic or ovate leaves were related to bay laurel (*Laurus nobilis*). The species was described in glowing terms by Philip Miller in his work *The Gardener's Dictionary* (see overleaf). Miller was Head Gardener at the Chelsea Physic Garden, Britain's second-oldest physic or botanic garden. His careful plant studies raised the reputation of Chelsea to one of the greatest gardens in Europe, and he published his thoughts in a single, detailed volume in 1731. This massive undertaking recorded all the cultivated plants in Britain at the time; during Miller's lifetime, it was republished in eight editions, each larger than the last. The first edition included *M. grandiflora* under the name *Tulipifera virginiana* (used for *M. virginiana* but with a supplementary description of this unnamed yet distinct plant). In later editions, Miller described *M. grandiflora* as a separate species under the rather cumbersome name *M. foliis lanceolatus persistentibus caule erecto arboreo*.

This predated the binomial system of plant naming introduced by Carl Linnaeus which we still use today. In fact, Miller was not a great supporter of the binomial system. Despite this, Linnaeus praised his work, describing *The Gardener's Dictionary* as a work "not merely … of gardening, but of botany". For scientific use, the name *M. grandiflora* L. is given the author abbreviation "L." – to signify Linnaeus as the first acknowledged publisher of this combination name, in the second edition of his *Species Plantarum* in 1759. Miller gradually adopted Linnaeus's names as each revised edition of *The Gardener's Dictionary* was published, including that of *M. grandiflora*.

OPPOSITE: *Magnolia grandiflora* from M. Catesby: *The Natural History of Carolina, Florida, and the Bahama Islands*, 1754.

ABOVE: *Magnolia grandiflora* by Georg Dionysius Ehret, from C. J. Trew and G. D. Ehret: *Plantae selectae*, 1754.

This truly magnificent tree originates in the southeastern United States, from Virginia south to Florida and west to Texas and Oklahoma. It can reach heights of 36 m (120 ft) in its native haunts, where it grows as a free-standing tree in lowland forest. In the past, magnolia's hard and durable wood has been used in furniture and veneers, although its slow growth has caused it to fall out of commercial fashion. The tree has a distinctive pyramidal habit and is clothed in long, ovate, glossy, deep-green leaves, each of which can be 20 cm (8 in) long. As an evergreen, it retains these year-round, shedding small numbers throughout the seasons. *M. grandiflora* produces large globular, fragrant, creamy-white flowers in summer and early autumn among its glossy foliage.

Today, gardeners know and appreciate many species of magnolia. Most are Asian in origin, with flowers on bare, deciduous branches in early spring. The characteristic they all share is their very primitive flower structure. Look at the fruits and you can see similarities to a conifer cone; the flower too essentially resembles a cone, surrounded by large, coloured petals. Magnolias were among the first flowering plants to evolve, with their flowers offering pollen to beetles in exchange for pollination rather than relying on the vagaries of the wind. It is a successful model, if unspecialized by comparison with other flowering plants, and the widespread appearance of magnolia in temperate woodlands is proof of that.

In Britain, *M. grandiflora* is often grown against a wall to provide it some protection against the cold; although it will grow as a free-standing tree, it can be very slow to do so. Against an east-, south- or west-facing wall, *M. grandiflora* will develop into a large, free-flowering shrub. Glossy green foliage and glorious creamy-white flowers look particularly magnificent against formal stone-walled buildings, such as the Mansion at Wakehurst (Kew's Sussex garden). Further south in Europe, huge pyramidal trees are a common sight. Around the globe, magnolia must be one of the most widely planted species – a testimony to this extraordinary plant's adaptability and beauty.

BELOW: Magnolia by an unknown Chinese artist, early 19th century.

TU

upon Mats in a fhady Place to dry; after which they fhould be put up in a dry Place, where Vermin cannot get to them, obferving to keep every Sort feparated; but they fhould not be kept too clofe from the Air, nor fuffered to lie in Heaps together, left they fhould grow mouldy, after which they commonly rot when they are planted again.

The Off-fets of thefe Roots, which are not large enough to produce Flowers the fucceeding Year, fhould be alfo put by themfelves, keeping each Sort diftinct: thefe fhould be planted above a Month earlier in Autumn than the blowing Roots, in particular Beds in the Flower-nursery, where they may not be ex-pofed to public View: but the Earth of the Beds fhould be prepared for them, in the fame manner as for larger Roots, tho' thefe muft not be planted above five Inches deep, and may be placed much nearer together, than thofe which are to flower; and in one Year moft of them will become ftrong enough to flower, when they may be removed into the Flower-garden, and placed in the Beds amongft thofe of the fame Kinds.

TULIPIFERA; The Tulip-tree.

The Characters are;

The Flower confifts of feveral Leaves, which expand in fuch a manner, as (by fome thought) to re-femble a Tulip; the Pointal rifes in the Centre of the Flower, furrounded by a great Number of Chives; and afterward becomes a fquamofe Fruit, or Cone growing erect: to thefe Marks may be added, The Leaves, for the moft part, being angular, the upper Part is hollowed as if cut off with Scifsors, terminating in two Points.

We have but one Species of this Tree; viz.

TU

TULIPIFERA arbor Virginiana. H. L. The Virginian Tulip-tree.

This Tree is very common in America, where it grows to a great Magnitude; but in England there are at prefent but very few of them which have arrived to any confider-able Stature. This was formerly kept in Pots and Tubs, and houfed in Winter with great Care, in which Management the Plants made but poor Progrefs, nor would ever have produced Flowers; but about fifty Years ago there was one of thefe Trees planted out in a Wildernefs in the Gardens of the Right Ho-nourable the Earl of Peterborough at Parfons-green near Fulham, which foon convinced the Curious of their Miftake in the Culture of this Tree, by the great Progrefs it made; and in a few Years after it produced Flowers. This Tree is yet ftand-ing, and annually produces a great Quantity of Flowers, though fome of the Branches begin to decay, which perhaps may have been oc-cafioned by its being too clofely furrounded with other Trees, whofe Roots are fo much entangled with thofe of this Tree, that they draw the Nourifhment of the Ground from it. In fome Years this Tree produces Cones; but they have not ever been perfected fo as to contain good Seeds.

There are fome other Trees of this Kind, which have produced Flowers feveral Years, though I be-lieve none of them are very large: the biggeft I have feen (excepting that at Parfons-green) is not more than thirty-five Feet high; whereas my Lord Peterborough's is upwards of fifty Feet high, and is propor-tionably large in the Trunk; but this has a naked Body near forty Feet high, all the Branches growing near the Top of the Tree, which might

THE

Gardeners Dictionary.

Containing the METHODS of
CULTIVATING and IMPROVING
THE
Kitchen, Fruit, and Flower-Garden,
AS ALSO THE
Phyfic-Garden, Wildernefs, Confervatory,
AND
VINEYARD.
In which likewife are Included
The PRACTICAL PARTS of HUSBANDRY;
and the Method of Making and Preferving WINES,
according to the Practice of Foreign Vignerons.

Abridged from the Two Volumes in Folio,
By the AUTHOR, PHILIP MILLER, F.R.S.
Gardener to the Worfhipful COMPANY of APOTHECARIES,
at their BOTANIC GARDEN, in Chelfea;

— Digna manet divini gloria ruris. Virg. Geo.

In THREE VOLUMES.
VOL. I.

The THIRD EDITION, Corrected;
And the Whole digefted into ONE ALPHABET.

LONDON:
Printed for the AUTHOR;
And Sold by JOHN and JAMES RIVINGTON, at the Bible
and Crown, in St. Paul's Church-yard.
M.DCC.XLVIII.

Pages from *The Gardener's Dictionary* by Philip Miller, 1731

In his monumental work *The Gardener's Dictionary*, Philip Miller wrote in great detail about all the plants he encountered. He described *Magnolia grandiflora* as an unknown species of *Tulipifera*, due to its similarity to the plant he called *Tulipifera arbor Virginiana* which we now know as *Magnolia virginiana*.

Despite these issues with plant naming, it is obvious Miller had a strong affinity to growing and studying plants, and his descriptions remain accurate even after a period of more than 250 years. In many ways, Miller can be said to have laid the foundations of the gardening nation that England has become.

20 *Magnolia campbellii* by Walter Hood Fitch, from J. D. Hooker and W. H. Fitch: *Illustrations of Himalayan plants*, 1855.

Gramineae
(Andropogoneae)

Zea Mays L.

MAIZE: A CEREAL BOUND FOR SUCCESS
ZEA MAYS

MARK NESBITT AND MARIA VORONTSOVA

Maize is by far the most important of the cereals, with over 1,000 million tonnes (984.2 million tons) harvested each year. However, it contributes fewer calories to the human diet than rice or wheat, as large quantities are grown for biofuels and animal feeds. Such diverse uses have long been characteristic of maize. During the 8,000 or more years since it was first taken into cultivation, farmers in the Americas have selected many different varieties of the plant. Maize types include flour corn, which can be ground into fine flour for tortillas; dent corn, which has a coarser meal, used for cornbread; sweetcorn, harvested immature and eaten while fresh, and popcorn, with a soft, starchy centre that produces steam and explodes when heated. With the exception of sweetcorn, maize grains share the advantages of all cereals (grass grains used as food): the grains are largely made up of dry, starchy endosperm and thus store and travel well, compared to root or fruit crops, for example. Furthermore, almost all cereals are annual plants and thus fit flexibly into agricultural systems, allowing rotation with other crops.

The origin of maize remained a mystery until the invention of DNA fingerprinting techniques in the 1980s. The flowers of maize are quite unlike those of other grasses. Male flowers form a "tassel" at the top of the plant, while female flowers are enclosed by modified leaves; the dangling stigma (or "silk") of female flowers then receives pollen from the male. The corn cob is made up of between eight and 20 rows of grains. For a century, botanists devised complex hybrids of different species to explain such an unusual grass, but DNA has clearly demonstrated that maize is the direct descendant of teosinte (*Zea mays* subsp. *parviglumis*). Maize must have been taken into cultivation in southwestern Mexico, where this wild grass grows. The genus most

OPPOSITE: *Zea mays*, from F. E. Köhler: *Medizinal Pflanzen*, 1890.

RIGHT: Maize, from S. Schedel: *Calendarium*, 1610.

closely related to *Zea* is *Tripsacum*, sometimes grown as a decorative plant for its unusual inflorescences; these also have separate male and female flowers.

Part of the grasses family, the Poaceae, maize is related to other important food plants including wheat, barley, rice, sorghum and millet. It is particularly closely related to sugar cane; both plants are members of a tropical lineage tribe called Andropogoneae. Like all members of this lineage, they have two flowers grouped together in every spikelet, and the spikelets are arranged in pairs. They also have a special photosynthetic system called C4 photosynthesis.

All plants use carbon dioxide from the atmosphere to create sugar molecules for food. This process, called photosynthesis, normally takes place in all the green cells of a plant leaf, in the same space used for respiration. The C4 system is a special adaptation to dry environments. In this system, leaf anatomy is arranged in a way that allows the plant to create higher concentrations of carbon dioxide away from oxygen,

increasing the efficiency of photosynthesis. A C4 plant can also carry out photosynthesis while losing less water, so it can carry on being productive in dry places.

Water supply is a critical issue for global food production. Efficient C4 photosynthesis in dry environments has helped maize to become one of the most successful food plants in the world. In many tropical countries, planting maize is the most reliable way to grow food almost anywhere. Human habitation in tropical Africa is usually accompanied by at least a few maize plants. Maize crops rarely fail and can be eaten by people and by animals. Human civilization relies on this valuable species.

ABOVE: Corn cobs collected at a local market, Huancayo, Peru, 1982. Kew Economic Botany Collection.

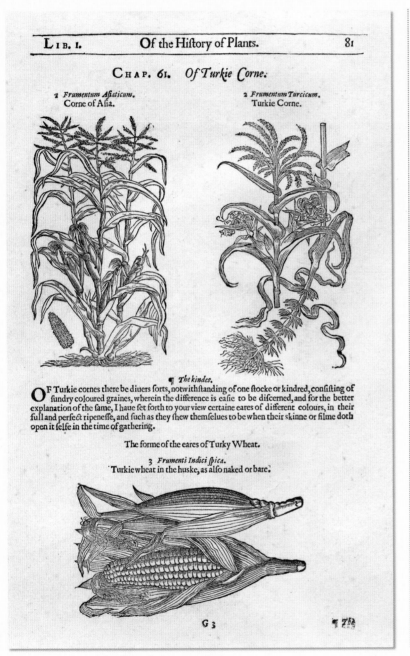

CHAP. 61.   *Of Turkie Corne.*

1 *Frumentum Aſiaticum.*
Corne of Aſia.

2 *Frumentum Turcicum.*
Turkie Corne.

¶ *The kindes.*

OF Turkie cornes there be diuers ſorts, notwithſtanding of one ſtocke or kindred, conſiſting of ſundry coloured graines, wherein the difference is eaſie to be diſcerned, and for the better explanation of the ſame, I haue ſet forth to your view certaine eares of different colours, in their full and perfect ripeneſſe, and ſuch as they ſhew themſelues to be when their skinne or filme doth open it ſelfe in the time of gathering.

The forme of the eares of Turky Wheat.

3 *Frumenti Indici ſpica.*
Turkie wheat in the huske, as alſo naked or bare.

G 3   ¶ Z⁵

Extract from *The Historie of Plants* by John Gerard, 1597

This page, taken from Gerard's herbal, depicts three types of "Turkish corn". During Gerard's time, maize became a staple crop in parts of Europe. It was thought to be spread by the Turks into European markets, hence the name used here by Gerard.

The title page of Gerard's herbal shows a classical figure holding flowers of snake-head fritillary and a giant corn cob, resembling a club. The figure combines a nod to history, in the form of Dioscorides, the Roman physician, and modernity, in the form of two plants both recently arrived in British gardens.

21   Various maize by Kan'en Iwasaki, from *Honzu Zufu*, 1828.

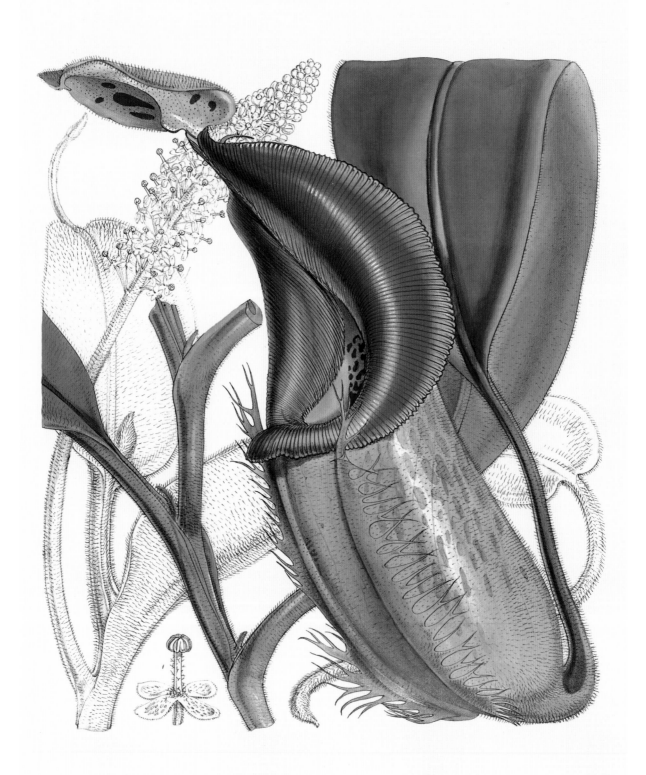

A BEAUTIFUL CARNIVORE
NEPENTHES

CHRISTINA HARRISON

With its gaping red mouth and grasping tendrils, you could be forgiven for recoiling from a pitcher plant. The sinister overtone of these weird-looking plants increases when you learn how they feed. There are currently 140 species in the genus *Nepenthes* (the figure is rising fast) and they are carnivores. Native to Southeast Asia, Meghalaya in India, Sri Lanka, the tip of Queensland, Australia, and Madagascar, this diverse group of plants thrives in tropical forests. They often grow in nutrient-poor soils, and so have evolved to digest insects (usually ants) and other wildlife to supplement their diets. As with all carnivorous plants, the ways in which *Nepenthes* trap their prey are gruesome and fascinating.

The one thing all *Nepenthes* have in common is their jug-like pitchers, which contain a soup of digestive juices. Each pitcher is actually an extension of the leaf. You can tell when a pitcher is developing as a swelling appears at the end of a leaf tendril; it expands and inflates before the lid finally pops open to reveal a pool of digestive liquid at the base. Unwary visitors are attracted to the rim of the pitcher – a colourful collar called the peristome, which can be brightly striped and grooved. There are glands on the collar that secrete sugary nectar to attract prey. The waxiness of the collar means that insects lose their footing easily and slip into the pitcher.

This genus varies greatly in size and colour. *Nepenthes rajah* from Borneo has the largest pitchers, able to hold up to 3.5 litres (6 pints) of water – enough to drown a rat. *Nepenthes rafflesiana* has evolved to emit a sweet scent from its mature pitchers, luring insects such as butterflies and beetles that usually visit flowering plants. Others, such as *N. lowii* and *N. hemsleyana*, offer shared rewards instead. *Nepenthes lowii*, from the cloud forests of Borneo, surprised the botanical world when it was discovered in 2009 to be offering a sugary lunch to mountain tree shrews. The creatures came to sit on the tough, wide-mouthed pitchers to lick the underside of the lids. They then used the pitchers as lavatories, so the plant gained vital nutrients from their droppings.

Such arrangements, it seems, are not that unusual – pitchers attract a wide range of animals: bats roost inside some pitchers, including *N. hemsleyana*; sunbirds in Africa, Southeast Asia, India and Australia are known to feed on pitcher-plant nectar, and some frog species are even known to use pitchers as spawning grounds.

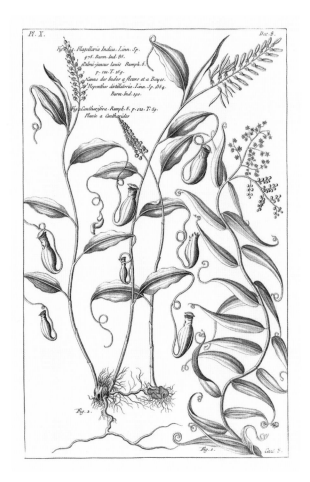

OPPOSITE: *Nepenthes villosa* by Walter Hood Fitch, from *Curtis's Botanical Magazine*, 1858.

ABOVE: *Nepenthes distillatoria* from, P. J. Buchoz: *Histoire universelle du règne végétal*, 1775–78.

Nepenthes have long fascinated scientists. Kew's connection with this genus dates back to 1789, when Sir Joseph Banks introduced the first species into cultivation in Europe – *N. mirabilis*. Although this specimen did not survive very long, it inspired plant hunters to collect more live plants for study, and for sale. Charles Darwin kept several pitcher plants in a hothouse at Down House in Kent. He wrote frequently about them to his friend Sir Joseph Hooker, Director of Kew, asking for specimens of *N. laevis* and *N. distillatoria* as he researched his new work, *The Movements and Habits of Climbing Plants*. Darwin enquired of Hooker whether pitcher plants climb by the tips of their leaves, to which Hooker replied that he had certainly observed them doing so. In August 1864, Hooker also wrote: "Nepenthes climbs famously by the stalk of the pitcher, and the pitcher fully develops after the process – it also thickens. Our Nepenthes have improved vastly since I first drew attention to them and they are clambering away by

said stalk beautifully." In 1872, Hooker wrote the first monograph of the genus, naming most of the more spectacular plants.

Kew's collection of these clever and captivating plants continues to grow, and new discoveries continue to be made about the genus. In 2013, Kew botanist Martin Cheek named 12 new species of *Nepenthes* from the Philippines. The following year, another new species, *N. zygon*, was discovered in Kew's Tropical Nursery, having arrived under the wrong name years before. Kew holds around 7 million herbarium specimens, some of which, including the aptly named *N. extincta*, are thought to be already extinct in the wild due to the destruction of their habitats.

BELOW: *Nepenthes bicalcarata* from *L' Illustration horticole*, 1871.

Singapore
26th Sep. 1874

D.r Hooker,

Dear Sir

This is the head of Nepenthes Seeds alluded to in my previous letter. I hope you will be successful in getting them to germinate —

I think that I have observed 3 kinds growing in our jungles. this head is what I have always considered to be the Rafflesiana. It was also growing in a swamp but on high & dry ground. before getting it (me Mr Collins & myself) had just passed through a very swampy place where they were growing

most luxuriantly & running up trees between 20 & 30 feet. Its same kind of Nepenthes I have seen growing beautifully in running water as deep as to take a man up to his neck. they delight in water: on dry ground they never grow tall. Have any of your correspondents noted to you branched cocoa

nut trees & 3 trees (O.N.) growing from one seed? here with one be seen — branched tree as yet shews no signs of fruit —
I remain dear Sir
Yours very truly
R. Jamie
Seeds

Letter from Robert Jamie to Sir Joseph Dalton Hooker,
from Singapore, 22 October 1874

Robert Jamie has sent what he believes to be the head of a *Nepenthes rafflesiana* from Singapore to Kew's Director Sir Joseph Dalton Hooker. Jamie thinks he has observed three kinds growing in the jungles and this head is what he considers to be *N. rafflesiana*. It was growing on high, dry land, not in a swamp. Jamie and his companion also walked through a swamp, where they observed a nepenthes growing high in the trees, which was the same kind Jamie has seen growing in deep, running water. Finally, Jamie asks if any of Hooker's correspondents have ever reported multiple "cocoanut trees" growing from the same seed.

22 *Nepenthes northiana* by Marianne North, 1881. Named after the artist by Sir Joseph Hooker.

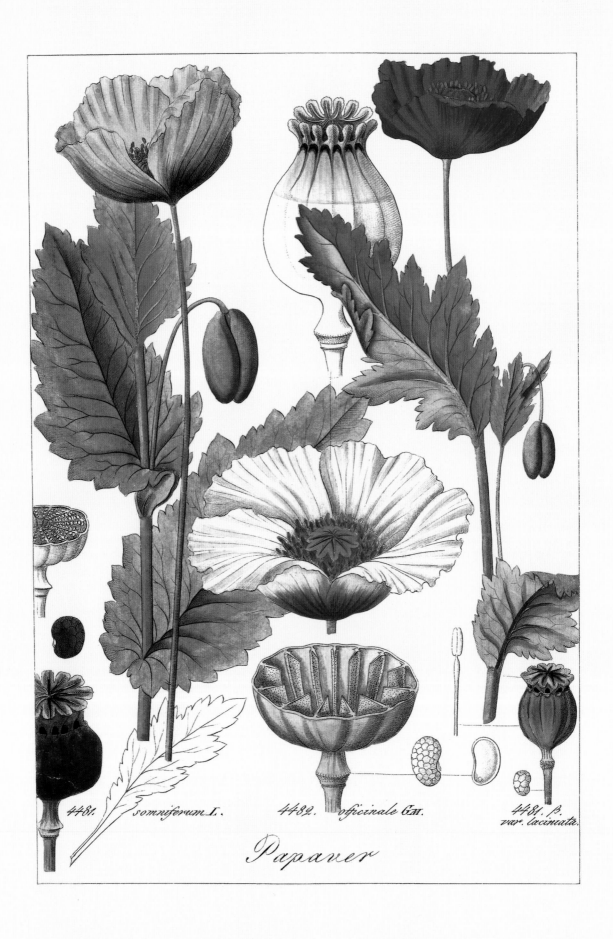

4481. *somniferum L.* *4482.* *officinale Gm.* *4481. β.*
var. laciniata.

Papaver

THE POWER OF POPPIES
PAPAVER

JAMES WEARN

....

There are approximately 70 species of poppy within the genus *Papaver*, but two are especially remarkable. The field or corn poppy (*Papaver rhoeas*) and the opium poppy (*P. somniferum*) are both familiar sights in gardens and on waysides, yet these simple plants have a rich and intriguing history, peppered with sad irony.

Both plants are annual herbs thought to have originated in southern Europe and temperate Asia, although they are now grown throughout much of Europe, Asia and North America. *Papaver rhoeas* has the scarlet flowers we traditionally associate with poppies, whereas there are hundreds of cultivars of *P. somniferum* resulting in a huge variety of colours and physical characteristics.

The field poppy has long been used for soothing aches and pains and as a mild sedative. It has been used for treating coughs and as a digestive – even for reducing the appearance of wrinkles and in lipstick. Traditionally, fresh petals are used to prepare a syrup, while dried petals are added to water to make an infusion. Chemical extracts from the petals have also been tested for their potential in the prevention of skin cancer. For example, a recent study found that field poppy extracts reduced the cellular effects of ultraviolet (UV) radiation.

The chemical power of the opium poppy is far greater than that of the field poppy because of the high quantities of potent narcotics in its white latex. This has led to its importance in medicine, but also to its exploitation through illicit trade. "Milk of the poppy" was prescribed liberally for centuries for virtually any illness. There is evidence of its use in prehistory, and the name for the poppy's sap, *opion* – still familiar to us today – was coined by the ancient Greeks. The morphine content of opium, an important chemical in the management of severe pain, is naturally between 9 and 14 per cent, but has been increased

OPPOSITE: *Papaver somniferum* from H. G. Reichenbach: *Icones florae germanicae et helveticae*, 1834–1914.

RIGHT: Kew Herbarium specimen of *Papaver rhoeas* collected from a former battlefield in Gallipoli by Lt Col Frank Durham, Director of Works at the Imperial War Graves Commission, 1925.

artificially in a cultivar selected to contain 91 per cent morphine, codeine and thebaine. The effects of morphine are now being explored in relation to the inhibition of tumour growth.

A set of impressive mahogany cupboards within the Herbarium at Kew significantly contains collections of both field and opium poppies. These were gathered together by Nathaniel Wallich, the botanist and surgeon of the East India Company. The Company produced most of the opium in India during the 18th century, with the poppies officially grown for medicinal use. However, an illegal drug trade flourished through devious channels, with the result that China in particular was supplied indirectly with opiates from the Company's plantations. China banned the sale and import of opium in an attempt to remove its corrupting influence, but complex networks were developed to circumvent these laws. Disputes escalated into two Opium Wars between Britain and China during the 19th century.

From 1914, morphine ampoules were needed to aid millions of soldiers injured in the First World War. This sudden and vital demand temporarily halted advances made in preceding years concerning the regulation of opiates. Alongside this, the field poppy was accorded a new duty, becoming the potent symbol of remembrance for millions of people. The war left people with more than tangible scars, including the emergence of "shell-shock" from the trenches. We wear our poppies to remember those who suffered, both outwardly and inwardly.

The opening lines of the poem "In Flanders Fields" by Lieutenant Colonel John McCrae (1915) earned the plant the colloquial name "Flanders poppy". Sadly, McCrae did not survive the conflict to see the powerful and far-reaching influence of his heartfelt words:

In Flanders fields the poppies blow.
Between the crosses, row on row …

The heavily churned soil, dug up to create trenches and tossed around by explosions on the battlefields, provided the stimulation required for the poppy seeds to germinate and spring into life. The vast swathes of red flowers became synonymous with "seas of blood". In 1917, Sir Arthur Hill, then Assistant Director of Kew, commented about the Somme area: "Nowhere, I imagine, can the magnitude of the struggle be better appreciated than in this peaceful poppy-covered battlefield hallowed by its many scattered crosses".

Even as their appearance became an overwhelming sight historically, it continues to evoke compassion, empathy, sorrow and hope a century on. The enduring remembrance encapsulated in delicate field poppy flowers is juxtaposed with the opium fields of Afghanistan today, giving the poppy's legacy a tragic contemporary twist. This is an ongoing tale of two common plants with a past and future no less colourful than their flowers.

BELOW: Ploughing the fields for opium cultivation in India, by an unknown local artist, on pith paper as a series of illustrations.

ROYAL BOTANIC GARDENS, KEW.

BULLETIN

OF

MISCELLANEOUS INFORMATION.

Nos. 9 & 10]   [1917

XXIX.—THE FLORA OF THE SOMME BATTLEFIELD.

The ground over which the Battle of the Somme was fought in the late summer and autumn of 1916 rises gradually towards Bapaume, and at the same time is gently undulating with some well-marked branching valleys initiating the drainage system of the area. Before the war the land was for the most part under cultivation, but on the highest levels there were large areas of woodland such as High Wood and Delville Wood, now shattered and destroyed, which will live as famous names in history.

The Butte of Warlencourt, reduced by bombardment to a bare mound of chalk, is seen by the remnants of stumps to have been covered with trees, and was no doubt just such a feature in the landscape as Barbury Camp or other clumps of trees on our English downs. Many an obscure village—and they were fairly numerous—has become immortal, but there is scarcely anything left to mark their site.

Villages, roads, open country, and woodland have been destroyed and ploughed up again and again by shells, with the result that hardly a level spot can be found. The surface of the ground is everywhere more or less deeply pitted by shell-holes of varying size and depth, and can best be imitated by arranging innumerable cups and basins as closely together as possible so that their rims shall reach a general level. It is only on the rims of the shell-holes that walking is possible.

During last winter and spring all this country was a dreary waste of mud and water, the shell-holes being so well puddled that the water has remained in them, and even in the height of the summer there were innumerable ponds, more or less permanent, in every direction.

The underlying rock is everywhere chalk with a covering of loam of varying thickness. As a result of the bombardment the old surface soil has been scattered and the chalk partially exposed. One effect of the shelling, however, has been to disintegrate the underlying chalk and produce a weathering effect which has been accentuated by the winter rains, snow and frost. A general mixing of chalk, subsoil, and scattered top soil and also a rounding of the sharp edges has taken place, so that

(5071.) Wt. 152—699. 1,125. 12/17. J. T. & S., Ltd. **G. 14. Sch. 12.**

Extract from "The Flora of the Somme Battlefield" by Sir Arthur Hill, *Bulletin of Miscellaneous Information,* 1917

Sir Arthur Hill (Kew's Assistant Director, 1907–22, and Director, 1922–41) was passionate about horticulture, earning himself and subsequent Directors of Kew the honorary title of "Botanical Advisor" to the Imperial (later Commonwealth) War Graves Commission. He was also intrigued by the flora which appeared following the destructive Battle of the Somme of 1916.

Hill felt the intensity of the scene which unfolded after the battle: "No more moving sight can be imagined than this great expanse of open country gorgeous in its display of colour, dotted over with the half-hidden white crosses of the dead."

During two brief visits to the area during the war, he recorded more than 25 plants, almost entirely annuals, which had sprung from the soil, of which the field poppy was the most striking and has become the most famous.

23 *Papaver somniferum,* from F. E. Köhler: *Medizinal Pflanzen,* 1890.

CAPTURING THE BLUE VANDA
VANDA COERULEA

LYNN PARKER

More than almost any other group of plants, orchids have elicited an obsessive desire to acquire them at virtually any cost. For much of the 19th century the preserve of the élite, the fascination for collecting these strange but beautiful flowers gave rise to "orchidelirium". Victorian orchid enthusiasts were eager to have unusual specimens, and nurserymen wanted to acquire striking species that would be useful for sale and hybridization.

Truly blue orchids are rare, and *Vanda coerulea*, an extraordinarily blue orchid, became something of a phenomenon when first publicized in Europe. It was initially discovered in the 1830s, in Assam in northeast India, by William Griffiths, a British doctor and naturalist. The Victorian nurseryman James Veitch sent his collector Thomas Lobb, who had met Griffiths in Singapore in 1843, to find this elusive orchid. He understood that its exceptional colour and beauty would be irresistible to aficionados. By 1849, Lobb had found the orchid and sent a substantial shipment of plants back to Veitch and, in December 1850, Veitch exhibited a flowering specimen at a meeting of the Horticultural Society.

That same year, Joseph Dalton Hooker referred to seeing *V. coerulea*, which he called "the most superb Orchid of this or perhaps any other county", near the village of Lernai: "We collected seven men's loads of this superb plant for the Royal Gardens at Kew, but few specimens reached England alive. A gentleman who sent his gardener with us to be shown the locality was more successful. He sent one man's [load] to England, and though it arrived in a very poor state, it sold for £300. Had all arrived alive they would have cleared £1,000. An active collector with the facilities I possessed might easily clear from £2,000 to £3,000 in one season by the sale of Khasia orchids."

Hooker's account reveals how desirable and valuable orchids had become, with many private collectors funding expeditions to collect prized blooms. This resulted in an unsustainable collection of orchids for commercial markets that decimated wild populations. Rare plants that could not be taken were often destroyed to prevent other collectors from obtaining them. Frederick Sander, "the orchid king", instructed one of his orchid collectors not only to collect the same type of flowers as a rival, but also, to ensure that he had the best plants, to destroy the other's specimens by urinating on them! Hooker deplored

OPPOSITE: *Vanda coerulea* by L. Constans, from J. Paxton and J. Lindley: *Paxton's Flower Garden*, 1853.

ABOVE: *Vanda coerulea*, artist unknown, late 19th century.

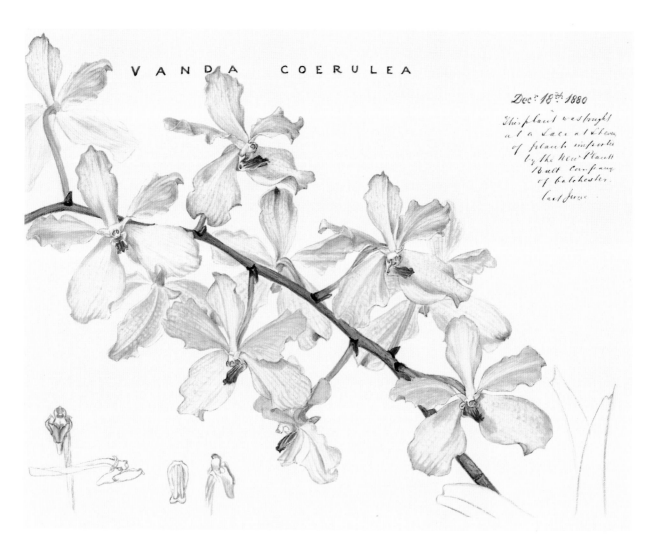

Decr 18th 1880

the extent to which orchids were taken, commenting that "the roads are all becoming stripped like the Penang jungles and I assure you for miles it sometimes looks as if a gale had strewed the road with rotten branches & Orchideae [sic]".

The English orchid collector John Day acquired his first 50 tropical orchids at an auction in 1852. He favoured more unusual species from India and the Americas, housing them in a specially built orchid house in the grounds of his home in Tottenham. Between 1863 and 1888, Day produced some 4,000 illustrations of orchid species in 53 scrapbooks. His sketchbooks provide a fascinating insight into the collection of a Victorian orchid enthusiast. Many depict plants that he had coaxed into flower; some are the earliest known images of particular species, while others are no longer in cultivation.

Day first drew *V. coerulea* in 1868, but was not satisfied. Another attempt in December 1880 produced a beautiful watercolour sketch of the species (see above), referred to in his notes as "this glorious thing, the most beautiful of all orchids (at all events the equal of any) I have at last had the courage to draw". As elegant as the drawing is – and the delicate textures and subtle shades of blue are executed with great skill – Day still felt that he had not quite captured the full magnificence of the exquisite bloom. "I am still far from doing it justice," he pronounced, "yet I have made a nearer approach now than I did then."

ABOVE: *Vanda coerulea* by John Day, from *John Day Scrapbook 27*, 1880.

Advertisements in *The Gardeners' Chronicle*, London, 1895

Exotic orchids were generally introduced to the public for sale at specialist auctions, as these advertisements from *The Gardeners' Chronicle* illustrate (see middle, top). Frederick Boyle, an orchid enthusiast, attended such a sale organized by Protheroe & Morris, recounting his experience:

"On tables of roughest plank round the auction-rooms are neatly ranged the various lots; bulbs and sticks of every shape, big and little, withered or green, dull or shining, with a brown leaf here and there, or a mass of roots dry as last year's bracken. No promise do they suggest of the brilliant colours and strange forms buried in embryo within their uncouth bulk… it was a great day indeed… It is astonishing to me that so few people grow orchids. Every modern book on gardening tells how five hundred varieties at least, the freest to flower and assuredly as beautiful as any, may be cultivated without heat for seven or eight months of the year."

His account conveys at once a sense of cynicism mixed with an undeniable admiration of the object of his desire.

24 *Vanda coerulea* by Walter Hood Fitch, from R. Warner and B. S. Williams: *Select orchidaceous plants*, 1862.

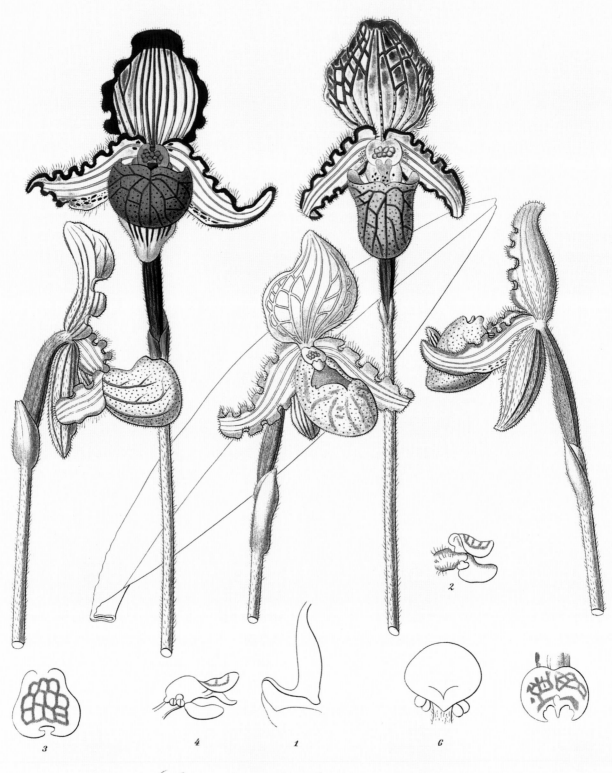

Cypripedium Fairieeanum Lindl.

ORCHID FEVER
PAPHIOPEDILUM FAIRRIEANUM

LAUREN GARDINER

Victorian "orchid fever" reached a peak in the 19th century as the British Empire expanded and the Industrial Revolution gathered speed. The wealthy could devote their disposable income to collect the ever more intricate and varied orchids that were being brought back from the tropics. These orchids were more often than not quickly killed in inappropriately sweltering and smoky "hothouses" – if they survived the long journey to England.

Kew's Herbarium, Archives and Illustration collections hold more than 100,000 orchid illustrations – many of them attached to herbarium specimens (dried pressed plants, which form the backbone of Kew's research collections) – and ephemera, such as a complete set of Wills's cigarette cards featuring orchids and dating from the early 1900s. More than a thousand images are the original illustrations of orchids printed in *Curtis's Botanical Magazine* (1787–1983). The collection is world renowned for the range and quality of the artwork and species represented.

Regarded today as the "father of orchidology", John Lindley was the leading orchid expert of the first half of the 19th century. He received specimens and correspondence from around the world: from collectors such as Nathaniel Wallich in India and Thomas Lobb in Java; from nurseries such as Loddiges in Hackney, London; and from botanists including Heinrich Gustav Reichenbach, who succeeded Lindley as Europe's foremost authority on orchids. Lindley published several thousand new orchid species and dozens of new genera during his lifetime, mostly in journals such as *The Gardeners' Chronicle*. One such species was the dramatic and striking *Paphiopedilum fairrieanum* in 1857 (see overleaf).

CYPRIPEDIUM FAIRIEANUM

OPPOSITE: *Paphiopedilum fairrieanum* (as *Cypripedium fairrieanum*), from H. G. Reichenbach and G. A. W. Arnott: *Xenia Orchidacea*, 1900.

RIGHT: *Paphiopedilum fairrieanum* (as *Cypripedium fairrieanum*), No. 4 of 26 orchid cigarette cards, from *Carreras High Class Cigarettes*, early 20th century.

Cypripedium Fairieanum in its native habitat.

Lindley's orchid herbarium contains more than 3,000 dried specimens, many including his own hand-drawn illustrations. Purchased by Kew in 1865, the herbarium was described by Kew's first official Director, Sir William Hooker, as "unique, its value can never diminish for it is a standard of reference, it can neither be imitated nor replaced. It must instantly be consulted as long as orchids are cultivated and Botany is a science."

In dedicating *P. fairrieanum* to Mr Fairrie of Liverpool, who exhibited it for the first time at the Royal Horticultural Society in 1857, Lindley described the plant (initially placed in the genus *Cypripedium*) as a "vegetable gem". With its white petals boldly marked with purple veins and hairs, distinctive S-shaped petals and its large, white dorsal sepal covered with a network of purple veins and pale green lip, the species is easy to identify. The first illustration, by the eminent Walter Hood Fitch, printed in *Curtis's Botanical Magazine* in 1857, shows its striking beauty.

The cool-growing orchid species is found in the wild in Sikkim, southern Bhutan and Arunchal Pradesh, usually on steep slopes, at altitudes of 1,400–2,200 m (4,500–7,200 ft). By the early 1900s, all the plants that had been brought back to England by the Victorian orchid hunters had been killed in cultivation – suffocated in the dank hothouses that horticulturalists of the time thought replicated the tropical climes where all such orchids surely thrived. Frederick Sander, the so-called "orchid king" from the Sanders & Co. nursery in St Albans, offered a reward of £1,000 for a plant of *P. fairrieanum* in 1905. Orchid collectors searched in earnest for "the thousand-pound orchid" in the wild, stripping forests of potential candidates and condemning most of these plants to certain death on the way to England, if not when they got there. Within three months of Sanders's appeal, the species had been rediscovered, but its identity was not confirmed until 1905, when some of the plants were flowered in Kew's glasshouses. Sanders's offer of such an enormous reward saw wild orchid populations in Asia irreversibly plundered. The hundreds of *P. fairrieanum* plants that made it back to Europe flooded the market, and by the end of 1905 the plants were selling for just a few shillings apiece.

LEFT, ABOVE: *Dendrobium lituiflorum* by Walter Hood Fitch, from *Curtis's Botanical Magazine*, 1873. *Dendrobium lituiflorum* grows in the same places as *Paphiopedilum fairrieanum* but is a very different type of orchid.

LEFT: *Paphiopedilum fairrieanum* (as *Cypripedium fairrieanum*), from *The Garden. An illustrated weekly journal of horticulture in all its branches*, 1883.

Extract from *The Gardeners' Chronicle*, 31 October 1857

Listed as *Cypripedium faireanum*, this new plant is described by editor John Lindley as "an exquisitely beautiful little species". Lindley founded the periodical *The Gardeners' Chronicle* with fellow horticulturists Joseph Paxton and Charles Wentworth Dilke in 1841. From 1986 onwards it has been known as *Horticulture Week*.

Aside from orchids, Lindley also published works on roses, the British flora, medicinal plants and botany in general, as well as collaborating on John Claudius Loudon's *Encyclopedia of Plants*. He is also known as the man who saved Kew. Following the deaths of Kew Director Joseph Banks and King George III in 1820, Kew began to fall into decline, and the government formed a committee which included Lindley to review the Gardens' purpose either as a Royal Household or as a place for scientific research and the public. In Lindley's report of 1838, he recommended that the Gardens be retained for the nation as a centre of botanical science equipped with a herbarium and library. The government did not accept the findings but the matter was put to Parliament in 1840. As a result Kew was able to continue and William Jackson Hooker was appointed Director in 1841.

25 *Paphiopedilum fairieanum (as Cypripedium fairieanum)* by Walter Hood Fitch, from *Curtis's Botanical Magazine*, 1857.

TRAVELLER OF THE TROPICS
COCONUT PALM

LAUREN GARDINER

Described variously as the "tree of life" or the "tree of a thousand uses", the coconut palm is instantly recognizable. It conjures images of tropical paradises around the world.

Carl Linnaeus knew of the coconut's existence from literary sources such as Rheede's *Hortus Indicus Malabaricus* (1678–1703). Although it is unlikely that he ever saw living plants, he published the genus and species names in his seminal work documenting his view of the world's plants, *Species Plantarum* (1753).

Strangely for such a distinctive and well-known palm, the geographic origins of the pan-tropical *Cocos nucifera* are still debated: it has been cultivated for so long and in so many places. The coconut's closest relatives are found in South America, but the major diversity in varieties and subspecies (many of which have been considered to be distinctive species in *Cocos* by different authors over the years) occurs in Southern Asia. The familiar "nut" of the coconut can travel enormous distances by floating in seawater, germinating months later on beaches, and recent research suggests that the plant evolved in coral atoll ecosystems in the Pacific.

Like many members of the palm family (Arecaceae, also known as Palmae), *C. nucifera* can be used by humans in a vast number of different ways. Traditional uses are particularly important for many communities around the world, hence its colloquial names. Timber for building, furniture, utensils, pots and handicrafts can be obtained from the dense solitary trunk, which grows up to about 30 m (100 ft) in height. The growing point at the top of the trunk (known as palm heart, or palmito) can be eaten, although this harvesting kills the plant. Leaves and their leaflets can be used as thatching and woven into barriers, thin walls, fences and roofs, baskets and flooring mats. Fibres from the leaf sheaths may be used to make brushes and brooms. The developing flowering stems (infloresences) can be tapped for their sugary sap, which can be made into an alcohol – either palm wine or a rather fiery palm toddy.

The familiar hairy, brown "nut" from the British fairground coconut shy is more akin to the stone of a peach than a true nut. Encased in a thick-walled fruit – usually green and ripening to yellow through to reddish-brown, depending on the coconut variety – the hard brown shell contains coconut flesh and water, along with the kernel itself (the seed). The fruit wall dries as the coconut ripens and ages, forming thick dense fibres; these are used to make rope, mats, rugs and carpets, often spun on traditional spinning wheels. The fibres and their dust are used as components of potting compost.

Each coconut has three large pores at one end of the fruit, through one of which the kernel germinates. The three pores, rather resembling a face, are thought to have given the palm its name *Cocos*, a Portuguese corruption of an aboriginal name for a monkey. Coconut flesh can be scooped out and eaten directly or dried to make desiccated coconut. It can be processed to extract oil for candles, soaps and a spreadable alternative to butter. Coconut milk and coconut cream are made from the shredded and squeezed flesh, while coconut water is a popular and healthy drink. Sterile, with a well-balanced mixture of salts and sugars, it is an excellent saline substitute for first-aid use in the tropics, as well as an electrolyte replacement for those who have overindulged in drinking their palm toddy.

The coconut palm is a great tree for agroforestry, with its many uses. The canopy produced by the leaves blocks out only 40–50 per cent of the light to the plants below, making it an ideal shade tree for many other crops, and it has only a limited root spread. *Cocos nucifera* can be sustainably grown, interspersed with a wide range of different cash and food crops. During the mid-1800s to late 1900s, colonial plantations of coconut trees as crop plants were created. Today, however, 95 per cent of coconut harvesting is done by small, independent growers, providing a source of life and livelihoods for many people around the world.

OPPOSITE: *Cocos nucifera* by Christabel King, from *Curtis's Botanical Magazine*, 1999.

ABOVE: *Cocos nucifera,* from H. A. van Rheede tot Drakestein: *Hortus Indicus Malabaricus,* 1678.

LEFT: *Cocoanut Palms on the coast near Galle, Ceylon* (Sri Lanka) by Marianne North, 1870s.

Pages from *Herbarium Amboinense* by Georgius Everhardus Rumphius, 1741–50

This six-volume work, by German botanist Georgius Everhardus Rumphius (1627–1702), was published during 1741–50, with text in parallel Dutch and Latin, and describes the flora of Amboina (Ambon island) in Indonesia. Despite the title, the plants covered in its volumes came from across the Dutch East Indies to Amboina, where Rumphius was based. Cited by Linnaeus and contemporaries, it is regarded as a key addition to the literature, with almost 1,700 plants described. In this extract, a description is given of coconut, accompanied by an illustration of the plant.

Employed by the Dutch East India Company, Rumphius was based in Amboina from 1653 until his death. He suffered many tragedies in his life, developing blindness around 1670 and losing his wife and eldest child in a huge earthquake in 1673. In 1687 a huge fire swept across Amboina and destroyed Rumphius's house, including manuscripts and illustrations for *Herbarium Amboinense*. Along with his son and other assistants, he produced the descriptions and illustrations once again, but these were then lost at sea when the ship carrying them was destroyed in transit. Thankfully, a copy had been made prior to despatch, and this was sent to Holland in 1696, where it remained in the archives of the Dutch East India Company until it was finally published in 1741.

26 *Cocus nucifera* from F. E. Köhler: *Medizinal Pflanzen*, 1890.

STEEPLES FROM THE ZAMBEZI DELTA
PANDANUS

DAVID GOYDER

The Scottish missionary and explorer David Livingstone had already traversed Africa from Luanda on the Atlantic coast to Quelimane on the Indian Ocean, writing up his journeys as *Missionary Travels and Researches in Southern Africa*, when the Royal Geographical Society in London put his name forward to lead the government-sponsored Zambesi Expedition of 1858–64. The expedition's aims were twofold: to establish settlements in malaria-free parts of the interior and to develop commercial activities that would reduce the influence of the East African slave trade in the region. Other resources were also to be documented with a view to development.

Things did not work out quite as planned, however. The Zambezi (widely spelled Zambesi at the time) was not as navigable a river as Livingstone had persuaded himself – he already knew about the barrier presented by the Victoria Falls, having seen "the smoke that thunders" during his coast-to-coast journey. But later on this expedition, further down the river, he had taken a route that diverged from the Zambezi. He thus missed a lower section of the river with the equally problematic Cabora Bassa rapids, and omitted to calculate the drop in altitude that would have indicated the presence of such rapids or falls.

Nevertheless, during the six years of the Zambesi Expedition, much valuable geographic and scientific information was gathered. Between 1,350 and 1,400 preserved plant specimens were gathered, mostly by Dr John Kirk, the doctor and botanist who was also Livingstone's deputy on the expedition. He made more than 300 technical drawings of plants to accompany these specimens. The plants were named by specialists at Kew over subsequent years, many representing species new to science. Unfortunately, one shipment, sent back to England aboard HMS *Sidon*, was mislaid in the Naval Dockyard in Portsmouth for 20 years, and did not reach Kew until 1883. The 1,350 to 1,400 specimens were pressed and dried, so not damaged by their dockyard stay, but the delay was an inconvenience to scientists, who were always eager for new material.

Today, paintings from the expedition are housed at the Royal Geographical Society, the Natural History Museum in London and the Royal Botanic Gardens, Kew. Thomas Baines, the official artist and store keeper for the expedition, painted scenes documenting significant events, scenery or particularly striking plants. One painting depicts John Kirk making a collection of *Pandanus livingstonianus* near the mouth of the Zambesi delta, while Baines himself appears by the stilt roots of a large specimen, sketching the plant. Another painting in Kew's collections portrays a village sugar factory further upriver. Here, groups of people are engaged in the various stages of sugar manufacture, from cutting the canes to evaporating the sugar.

In a review of tropical African screw pines in 1896, this species of *Pandanus* was described as new to science, based on a dried fruit preserved in the Economic Botany Collection at Kew. Its name commemorates David Livingstone, on whose expedition it was discovered. In his book *Narrative of an Expedition to the Zambesi and its Tributaries*, published in 1865, Livingstone described these plants "appearing as tall as in the distance to remind us of the steeples of our native land".

Livingstone's *Pandanus* reaches up to about 20 m (65 ft) tall, with a columnar or narrowly pyramidal outline, when it grows unrestrained by other trees. It has a very characteristic habit, with tufts of large spirally arranged leaves at the end of the main stem and smaller tufts terminating the branches. It also has sturdy stilt roots, and all parts are covered with stiff prickles. Male and female flowers are produced on different plants, and the compound fruit resembles a small pineapple, with its tessellated surface.

Despite appearances, pandans are not closely related to the palm tree – but they do have economic potential. Growing on seasonally inundated rivers in the delta, the timber is resistant to termite attack, as are other mangrove timbers. The leaves are used to make a variety of mats and fibres, in much the same way as palm fronds can be broken down into strips, which are then woven into bags and other products. Leaves of related species are also used to flavour food in Southeast Asian cuisine.

OPPOSITE: *Ripe fruit of screw pine*
(*Pandanus tectorius*) by Marianne
North, late 19th century.

LEFT: *Study of screw pine* by Marianne North, late 19th century.

BELOW: Fruit head of *Pandanus livingstonianus* collected by John Kirk, 1883. Kew Economic Botany Collection.

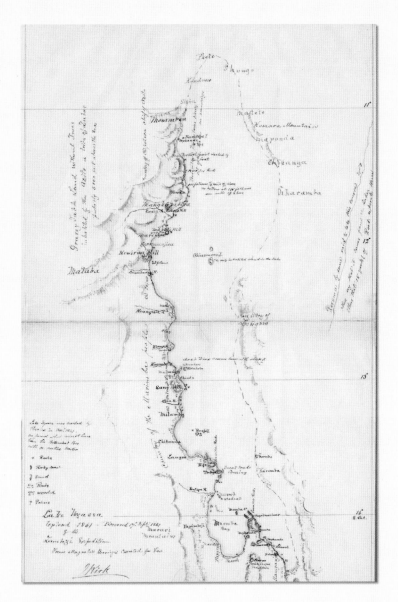

Map from John Kirk to Sir William Jackson Hooker, from the Zambezi Expedition, 1860

This very detailed map by Kirk of Lake Nyassa (now known as Lake Malawi) and its surroundings gives names of villages, rivers, hills and mountains around the lake, as well as the name of the main tribes inhabiting the area. The map has various handwritten notes, including:

"Lake Nyassa was reached by Roscher in Nov. 1861. We found what must have been his Botanical Box with a native trader."

"Lake Nyassa Explored 1861 – Discovered 17 Sep. 1861 by the Zambezi Expedition."

A note on the reverse of the map reads:

"Map of lake Nyassa as far as explored Sep. and Oct. 1861. From Corrected Magnetic Bearings." [Signed J.Kirk]

27 *Pandanus or screw palm covered with climbing plants, near the Kongone Canal of the Zambesi* by Thomas Baines, from D. Livingstone: *The Zambesi Expedition of David Livingstone*, 1858.

WEAVING FABRIC FROM THE STUFF OF LIFE

PAPER MULBERRY

MARK NESBITT

When we think of plant materials, many may spring to mind: wood, such as oak timber; leaves, such as banana leaves; or stems, such as bamboo. Outside the tropics, however, few are familiar with another plant material: inner bark. This is made up of the phloem tubes that carry sugars produced in photosynthesis from the leaves of a woody plant to its roots. The inner bark lies between the corky, outer bark that we all know and the woody stem. In a select few species of tree and shrub, mainly found in the tropics, this bark can be easily peeled off and used for various purposes. Paper mulberry is the most important source of inner bark in the Pacific region. It was beaten into barkcloth to form the traditional *tapa*, the main textile in Pacific islands prior to the arrival of European missionaries in the 19th century, who introduced woven textiles such as cotton. Paper mulberry is also the most important source of fibre for *washi*, handmade Japanese paper.

Paper mulberry is closely related to the true mulberry, *Morus*, and both genera are in the Moraceae family. Paper mulberry is native to Japan, Taiwan and China, and was carried by canoe into Polynesia and Melanesia thousands of years ago. In the wild, and when planted in gardens, it can grow up to about 20 m (65 ft) high, with attractive orange-red fruits. The leaves are often lobed, like the leaves of the fig tree. When cultivated for its inner bark, the tree is coppiced every 12–18 months, allowing the inner bark to be easily stripped from the young stems and separated from the outer bark. Paper mulberry bark is thus a highly sustainable material, as the tree can be coppiced indefinitely.

In the Pacific islands, the inner bark is cleaned and flattened with wooden beaters, then hammered or glued together to make large pieces. *Tapa* is of huge symbolic and religious importance, particularly in gift giving, and very large pieces are made for special occasions. The fabric can be beaten very fine and left undecorated, or may be painted or printed with coloured patterns. Some islands, such as Tonga and Samoa, still have thriving *tapa* traditions, but in many both the craft and the tree are in decline. However, there has been a revival of interest in their traditional crafts among the indigenous peoples of the Pacific, with particular emphasis on rediscovering ancestral *tapa* cloths now held in European and American museums. *Tapa* is a very portable

OPPOSITE: *Broussonetia papyrifera* by J. Curtis, from *Curtis's Botanical Magazine*, 1823.

ABOVE: Parasol made of *Broussonetia* paper and collected by Sir Harry Parkes in Japan, 1870. Kew Economic Botany Collection.

material and was often collected by 19th-century travellers; it is no surprise to find that Kew holds a rich collection of more than 70 pieces.

In Japan, paper mulberry (known as *kozo*) is also coppiced, but the harvested and cleaned inner bark is boiled and beaten to break up the fibres. These are then suspended in water. A mesh tray is used to pick up the fibres, which form a paper sheet. Handmade paper (*washi*) is exceptionally strong, and has found a modern use in the repair of historic books and papers. As in the case of tapa production, *washi* making is very labour intensive, and the number of makers is declining. Nonetheless, some 800 kinds of *washi* are still made – some plain, some dyed or printed and some with inclusions such as flowers or, in a modern innovation, fibreglass.

In 1870, Sir Harry Parkes, the British ambassador to Japan, was asked to investigate the production of *washi* on behalf of British paper manufacturers. Much of his collection ended up at Kew, including objects such as hats, a telescope, a toy box and sumptuous gilded sheets intended as wallpaper. This collection forms one of Kew's greatest treasures, attracting increasing numbers of visitors from Japan.

ABOVE: Illustrations of local paper making, from H. S. Parkes: *Reports on the manufacture of paper in Japan: presented to both Houses of Parliament by command of Her Majesty*, 1871.

Inclosure 3.

A short Account of the Manufacture of Paper in Japan, by Consul Lowder.

THE manufacture of paper from the paper mulberry (*Broussonetia papyrifera*) was introduced into Japan about A.D. 610. Up to the year A.D. 280, silk with a facing of linen was used for writing upon, and thin wood shavings were also employed. In that year, however, paper was imported from the Corea, and this appears to have been the only paper known to the Japanese until the year 610, when two priests named Donchô and Hôjô were sent over to Japan by the King of the Corea. Donchô is said to have been a clever man, learned in the Chinese classics, and moreover a skilful artist. Besides the manufacture of paper he also introduced that of writing-ink and mill-stones into the country. Shôtoku Taishi, a son of the reigning Mikado, learned of Donchô how to make paper. But although the paper made by Donchô was very good of its kind, it did not take ink well; it would not bear rough handling and tore very easily; and moreover it was liable, because of its material, to become worm-eaten, seeing which, Taishi introduced the manufacture of paper out of the paper mulberry; he made four kinds, called Unshi, Shiku-inshi, Haku-jushi, and Zoku-hakushi, and he caused the paper mulberry to be extensively planted all over the country, and the mode of paper manufacture to be largely promulgated among the people.

The Paper Mulberry, or Broussonetia Papyrifera (Ma Kôdzu).—(Illustration No. 1.

In the Island of Kiusiu the makôdzu is planted in the ninth and tenth moons, but in Kioto and its vicinity in the first moon, the time varying according to the climate of the place. Some old roots are separated and cut down to a length of about three inches; hese are planted so that a little less than half-an-inch appears above ground. They will grow about a foot high in the first year, and in the second they will rise to a height of two or three feet. In the third year they will reach a little over four feet; in the fourth year they attain to six, or if particularly fine, to even nine and twelve feet. Each year in the tenth moon they are cut down to the roots, and from each stalk five branches appear the next year, so that in five years a large and dense shrub is developed. The cuttings of the fifth year's growth are used for making paper. The roots will not thrive well in old ground; the best place for planting is round the edges of new-made ground or paddy-fields. They will not stand salt or brackish water, nor will they flourish beside millet or sorghum. Care must be taken not to over or under manure them; if under manured they die, and if too much manure is used the plant is injured. If planted in the vicinity of other crops, such as rice, they rejoice in the effects of the manure which is used for their neighbours. They are sometimes planted on mounds which are raised along the beds of valleys, but newly-turned ground is the best.

Cutting the Paper-Mulberry in Winter.—(Illustration No. 2.)

The paper-mulberry suffers from sun-burn in a very dry summer; and, on the other hand, if there is too much rain it grows too fast, and is then injured by the autumnal winds. Care must be taken to protect the plants from the ravages of wild boar and deer, which delight to feed upon them. The shrub known as "Ts'kuri-kake" is the best for making paper of, but it is scarce and expensive. There is also a variety called "kajiso," which makes good paper, but as it is more plentiful it is not so dear, though it is necessary to use a great deal of it. Another variety is called "takaso." Paper made of this is somewhat inferior, but the shrub attains a great height, and it is not necessary to divide the roots; a cutting of it may be planted just as it is cut, and will thrive, and it does not require so much attention as the "makôdzu" as regards manure; it will also thrive in swampy ground. It needs little care, and produces a tolerably large quantity of material for paper; and at present this variety is largely cultivated. The shrubs, like other trees, bud in spring, blossom in summer, and cast their leaves in autumn : by the twelfth moon they are quite bare.

Steaming the Paper-Mulberry.—(Illustration No. 3.)

The diameter of the boiler is 2 feet 6 or 7 inches; the steaming vessel is of straw. The mulberry stalks are cut into lengths of two and a-half to three feet for steaming. When the skin of the stalk begins to separate at the cut ends they are sufficiently steamed. Five or six steamings can be performed during a winter's night.

Stripping the Skin from the Stalk.—(Illustration No. 4.)

The stalks after steaming are taken in the hand as above illustrated, and the skin stripped off. After stripping the stick is of no use but for firewood.

Drying the Skins.—(Illustration No. 5.)

After peeling, the skins should be at once dried. They are divided into portions of a thickness that a woman can grasp conveniently in one hand. They are then hung on transverse poles and tied loosely at the ends, as in the illustration, so that the part tied may not be prevented from drying. They take ordinarily two or three days to dry, but if there is any wind they may dry in a day. After drying, they are weighed into portions of about 32 lbs. avoirdupois, and tied up in bundles.

Washing the Skins.—(Illustration No. 6.)

They are then ready for the next process, which is to wash them in running water in which they are left, as illustrated, for a day or a night, but twenty-four hours' washing will not hurt them. They are then taken in, and the inner fibre is separated from the outer skin.

Removing the Inner Fibre.—(Illustration No. 7.)

The outer dark skin is scraped off with a knife, as in the illustration, the knife being held stationary, pillowed on a straw padding, while the material is drawn towards the operator until the dark skin is removed. This dark scraping is used for making inferior kind of paper, known as "chiri-gami," and also "kizo-suki." It is called "saru-kawa," and after being thoroughly washed in running water, which causes it to open out flat, it is boiled. It is then allowed to rot, and is well beaten, after which

Extract from *Reports on the manufacture of paper in Japan: presented to both Houses of Parliament by command of Her Majesty, 1871* by Sir Harry Parkes

In this extract from Parkes's report, an account is given of the paper manufacture from paper mulberry in Japan, which it states was introduced into the country in about AD 610. The illustrations on the opposite page accompany this text and depict the scenes described.

Parkes was the British minister in Tokyo and in 1869 received a request from the British Foreign Secretary to prepare a report on Japanese handmade paper, or *washi*, and papermaking techniques. The British government was keen to learn of alternative papermaking techniques, as the primary source of fibre for papermaking, cotton and linen rags, had been in short supply since the 1840s. The report was presented to both Houses of Parliament with a variety of *washi* samples, which were later divided between the Victoria and Albert Museum (then the South Kensington Museum) and Kew, where they are housed in the Economic Botany Collection.

28 *Broussonetia papyrifera* by Pierre Joseph Redouté, from P. J. Redouté: *Traité des arbres et arbustes*, Nouvelle édition, 1804.

Passiflora quadrangularis

POWER AND GLORY:
THE CLIMBING PASSIONFLOWER
PASSIFLORA

CHRISTINA HARRISON

Exotic, beautiful, flamboyant, intricate: passionflowers are some of the world's most stunning climbing plants. It may surprise you to discover that there are more than 500 species of *Passiflora* and around 400 hybrids. They make beautiful additions to our gardens, but we grow relatively few in the UK, mainly *Passiflora caerulea*. Only a handful of species are truly frost-hardy, and they rarely produce their famed succulent fruits here. Most passionflower species hail from the tropical forests of South and Central America, ranging from perennial woody lianas that stretch up to 40 m (130 ft) into the tree canopy to delicate, knee-high annuals. However, most grow just a few metres in height and usually grow in the dappled light of forest margins.

Europeans first learned of the beauty of passionflowers after the Spanish conquistadors reached South America in the 16th century. Early explorers called them *granadillas*, or "small pomegranates", while the native peoples called them *maracocks*. Only in the early 17th century were passionflowers brought back to be cultivated in Europe's botanical gardens. It is thought the first (possibly a *P. incarnata*) was grown in Paris in 1612, soon followed by others as news of its beauty and alleged uses spread. The plant's symbolism helped its popularity, as Spanish priests named the flower after the mysteries of Christ's Passion. Its five sepals and five petals represented the ten disciples at the Crucifixion and the ring of corona filaments the crown of thorns. In the centre of the flower, the five stamens symbolized the five wounds suffered by Christ on the Cross, and the three stigmas the nails.

The desire to grow and create hybrids and cultivars of these wonderful plants is not hard to understand. Their variety of size, form and colour is breathtaking, adding an instant tropical flavour to any display. Beautiful flowers are complemented by attractive foliage, curling tendrils and colourful autumn fruits. New species are still being discovered; in 2009, scientists from Kew found a new, red-flowered species in the forests of the Brazilian Amazon, which they named *P. cristalina*.

Passionflowers have long been used in folk medicine as a diuretic, analgesic, antispasmodic and sedative. Some proof has been established of their mild sedative effects, but it is not clear which of the many chemical compounds they contain produces such effects. *Passiflora*

OPPOSITE: *Passiflora quadrangularis* from N. J. von Jacquin: *Selectarum stripium Americanarum historia*, 1839.

ABOVE: *Passiflora vitifolia* by Walter Hood Fitch, from *Curtis's Botanical Magazine*, 1852.

LEFT: *Passiflora amabilis* by
Walter Hood Fitch, from *Curtis's
Botanical Magazine*, 1848.

incarnata has been used in teas and herbal medications to treat stress and is sometimes offered alongside other herbal sedatives, such as lemon balm and valerian. However, as most parts of passionflowers contain cyanogenic glycosides (a source of cyanide), the herbal use of their leaves, roots or unripe fruits is not recommended.

The fruits of many species are delectable when ripe, although only a handful are grown commercially for their berries. In the wild, these are feasted on by monkeys, bats, tapirs and other animals, as well as many birds. The flowers (usually open only for one day) often need to be cross-pollinated by insects, hummingbirds or bats to produce these fruits. The most famous of the fruit-bearing species is the purple passionflower (*P. edulis*), of which there are around 100 varieties. The giant granadilla (*P. quadrangularis*) is grown around the world for its fruit; the largest in this genus, each grows to 2–3 kg (4½–6½ lb). The taste of passionfruits depends on the species, where they are grown, the climate and ripeness. In temperate climates such as the UK, one can successfully grow some species of passionflower on sheltered south-facing walls, but most species will only produce edible fruits in a greenhouse – and then only *P. edulis* is reliable.

Many *Passiflora* enthusiasts grow a selection of species in greenhouses alongside the insects that have co-evolved with them – the neotropical *Heliconiiae* butterflies. In the wild, these colourful, slow-flying and long-lived butterflies only lay eggs on particular *Passiflora* species. The plants have evolved to produce small spots on their leaves resembling butterfly eggs, to deter these visitors from laying any of their own.

Letter from Anna Maria Walker to Sir William Jackson Hooker, from Colombo, Ceylon (now Sri Lanka), 15 November 1834

Anna Maria Walker, a Scottish botanist and botanical artist in Sri Lanka (at that time known as Ceylon) writes to Hooker as Professor of Botany, University of Glasgow, prior to his Directorship of Kew. Walker sends him a few seeds in the hope that they arrive fresh. She wanted to send the whole seed vessel of the little *Passiflora*, but it is not sufficiently dry. She cannot help but think that the colouring matter it contains is valuable as a paint or dye and she sends a piece of paper smeared with it. She is sure that if found useful, the plant could be cultivated there: the plants she has transplanted have thrived.

In the parcel, seed pods of vanilla are also sent, of which she encloses a drawing. They have never seen the plant or flower that bears the long pods of the vanilla. Walker feared that, by keeping them until the Colonel's [her husband] plants were dry enough to send, there would be less chance of their vegetating. In September she dispatched drawings. She asks Hooker to give the seeds of the *Nepenthes* to Dr Graham who is anxious to see them. She has sent them frequently before but has never heard of them vegetating.

29 *Passiflora caerulea* by James Sowerby, from the first volume of *Curtis's Botanical Magazine*, 1787.

Fig. 1.

Fig. 2.

Fig. 3.

PÆONIA MOUTAN.   PIVOINE MOUTAN.

PROUD HERALDS OF SPRING
PEONY

RICHARD WILFORD

For a brief few weeks in late spring, the flowers of peonies light up the garden. Their blooms have a radiance rarely matched by other flowers at this time of year. Peonies range from small herbaceous species only 30 cm (1 ft) tall to majestic tree peonies reaching up to 2 m (6 ft 6 in) or more in height, with wonderfully flamboyant flowers. When you see these majestic blooms, you can understand why the Chinese called the tree peony the "king of flowers".

Peonies are naturally distributed across the Northern Hemisphere, with the majority occurring in Europe and temperate Asia. Tree peonies, known as *mudan* or *moutan* in Chinese, can make large shrubs with woody stems, but the herbaceous peonies die down to fleshy, tuberous roots in mid to late summer; they reappear in late winter and spring as bright red or purple shoots. Peonies have been cultivated in China for thousands of years, and in the 8th century the Japanese imported both herbaceous and tree peonies from China. They are still widely grown in Japanese gardens. In Britain, it is the herbaceous peonies that are more commonly seen, usually growing in sunny borders alongside other spring perennials.

In medieval times, herbaceous peonies were highly valued in Europe as medicinal plants. Properties of the roots included the relief of stomach pains and the curing of kidney and bladder complaints. The two species used in medicine at that time were both native to Europe: *P. officinalis* (called the female peony) and *P. mascula* (the male peony). The term *mascula*, meaning male, was used to distinguish robust species from more delicate ones. Later, in 1579, John Gerard's herbal devoted four pages to the peony. He notes that: "The black grains (seeds) to the number of fifteen taken in wine or mead … is a special remedy for those that are troubled in the night with the disease known as Ephialtes or nightmare."

By the late 18th century, several more herbaceous species were being grown in England, collected by travellers and brought back to be planted in gardens. These included *P. tenuifolia*, *P. peregrina* and *P. anomala*. Peony breeding took off in the 19th century, and reached its peak at the end of that century, particularly in France, where many new varieties were produced by great peony dynasties such as the Lemoine and Rivières families. Some famous peonies bred in France at that time are still going strong today, such as "Festiva Maxima" (1851), "Duchesse de Nemours" (1856) and "Sarah Bernhardt" (1906). By this time, peonies were largely grown in Europe for their beautiful flowers rather than medicinal purposes. The 20th century saw the popularity of peonies wane slightly, but there now seems to be a revival in interest, with borders or gardens devoted to them.

Peony species have wide, bowl-shaped flowers. In cultivation, there are also many double- and semi-double-flowered cultivars, however, mostly derived from the Asian *P. lactiflora*. These are often scented, and among the most commonly grown are "Sarah Bernhardt", which has large pink flowers, and "Festiva Maxima", with fragrant pale-pink flowers fading to creamy white, but there are many more. Forms of *P. officinalis* are also widespread, such as the dark purple "Anemoniflora Rosea" and the bright-red double-flowered "Rubra Plena". Simple, bowl-shaped blooms can be just as beautiful and include the striking magenta-pink "Hit Parade", with a boss of golden-yellow stamens at its centre, and the wonderful "Claire de Lune" with wide, creamy-yellow petals.

Some of the most glorious blooms belong to the tree peonies. When you come across magnificent plants such as the Chinese *P. rockii*, with its sumptuous, dark-centred, creamy-white blooms, you will realize why "king of flowers" is such a fitting name.

OPPOSITE: *Paeonia suffruticosa* (as *Paeonia moutan*) by Pancrace Bessa, from H. L. Duhamel du Monceau: *Traité des arbres et arbustes, Nouvelle édition*, 1819.

LEFT: *Paeonia* from S. Schedel:
Calendarium, 1610.

First and last pages of a six page letter from William Fullerton MacTier to the
Royal Botanic Gardens, Kew, from Kinnessburn, St Andrews, Fife, 19 May 1899

MacTier's son, an officer in one of the Native Regiments at Chitral (Pakistan), has just sent home some seeds of a white peony growing in the hills above his station at an elevation of 2,100–3,000 m (7,000–10,000 ft). As his correspondent may not have received many items from this out-of-the-way and troubled part of India, MacTier sends a supply, hoping they may be of interest. MacTier reproduces two short extracts from his son. The first is dated 15 August 1898 at 2,400–2,800 m (8,000–9,000 ft). Lieutenant MacTier finds himself amongst cedars, vines and walnuts, with English flowers in wild profusion. There are large white mallow roses, St John's wort, forget-me-nots, ragweed and great masses of pure-white-flowered peonies. Another extract dated 4 September notes that Lieutenant MacTier climbed up to a lonely open grassy plateau, at 3,700 m (12,000 ft), which was covered with flowers.

30 *Paeonia daurica* by Sydenham Teast Edwards, from *Curtis's Botanical Magazine*, 1812.

BOT. MAG.: Original Drawing.

Purchased of Mr. F. CURTIS, 1891.

PHOENIX FROM THE ASHES
PROTEA

TONY REBELO

The great botanist Carl Linnaeus named the protea family (the Proteaceae) after the Greek god Proteus, who could change his shape and foresee the future, but was unable to lie. However, Linnaeus inexplicably confused his names, calling the king protea (now *Protea cynaroides*) *Leucadendron* (meaning "white tree") and giving the silvertree (now *Leucadendron argenteum*) the name *Protea*. In this, he may have been confused by his best references to this family: Boerhaave's *Index Alter Plantarum*, published in 1727, erroneously referred to the cone of a *Leucadendron* developing out of the head of a *Protea*. When Linnaeus fixed his mistake, by swapping the names, all he offered by way of explanation was "*imo Proteo ipso magnis variabili & differente*", meaning that they were greatly variable and different.

The Proteaceae are an unusual family of basal eudicots – a form of plant that evolved early on, with diverse and experimental arrangements of parts. The family comprises woody shrubs and trees specializing in sites on nutrient-poor soils. The majority of species occur on the quartzitic sands of Australia and the Cape Flora, South Africa, although some also occur in South America, across Africa and north to Japan. As a consequence of living in poor soils, species are able to produce a surfeit of carbon, but their lack of nitrogen and potassium prevents them from making many leaves. All plant parts thus tend to be robust, woody and long-lived. This applies especially to the flowers, which often occur in dense flower heads; they produce copious nectar suitable for pollination by birds, rodents and marsupials. The style, the stalk of the carpel, is also robust. It is modified at the tip to hold the pollen as the petals fall away, forming a pollen presenter that brushes pollen on to the large and rough heads and bodies of pollinators.

Even seed dispersal is geared to low nutrients. Many species retain the fruit in the old flower heads, forming fireproof cones that are stored on the plants for release after fire (a process known as serotiny). Indeed, Linnaeus might equally have called the protea family after the phoenix, so intimately are their life cycles tied to the 10–50-year fire cycles of their communities. In addition to serotiny, many species utilize ants and rodents to bury and cache their seeds in fire-safe burrows, with germination only occurring after fires have taken place. In the genus *Leucospermum*, the "white seeds" are the ant-fruit covering (made

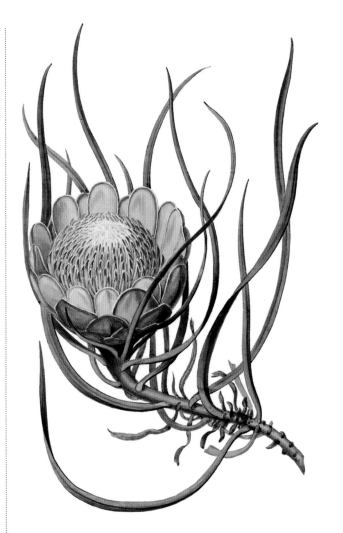

OPPOSITE: *Protea compacta* (as *Protea formosa)* from *Curtis's Botanical Magazine*, 1815. It accompanied the facsimile article overleaf.

ABOVE: *Protea laevis* by Sydenham Teast Edwards, from *Curtis's Botanical Magazine*, 1823.

from lipids and known as an elaiosome). This attracts ants and causes them to bury the fruit. The actual seeds beneath are hard and black; ants cannot grasp them and so are unable to discard the seeds from their nests afterwards, allowing them to germinate and grow.

An enigmatic feature of proteas is the wood of which they are made. Known as "silky oak" because of extensive medullary rays (radial sheets of conducting tissue), these leak water so freely that it is impossible to use protea wood for buckets or pots. Why protea wood is so porous is unknown.

Early botanists noted that plants of the Proteaceae are unusual in another way. During the hot, dry Mediterranean summers, when all others in diverse families have gone dormant, the proteas alone produce new growth in abundance. While other plants are unable to sustain normal physiological processes, proteas continue growing, producing soft new growth for expansion and hardening. This is achieved by a very deep root system that taps the deep water table, well beyond the reach of other plants, during summer.

Proteas are equally strange underground. Whereas most other plants utilize fungi to help them extract nutrients from the soil, the Proteaceae have no such associations. Instead, they produce highly specialized root systems: dense little root clusters with a total surface area of a tennis court (in this they are similar to Restionaceae and some Cyperaceae). It is thought that this strategy avoids wasting nitrogen on growing fungi. These proteoid roots use some of the water from the deep roots and flood the soil just under the surface. At the same time, they release strong acids and fungicides, killing microbes in the area and freeing more minerals in the soil. Nutrients are absorbed by the roots and used for further growth. This same process also allows protea tap roots to "drill" through solid ironstone and limestone, and so reach down to the deep waters beneath.

We are still woefully ignorant of all the specializations that the Proteaceae employ to survive. But, like the Proteus legend, if we continue to grasp these fascinating plants, and to ask them the correct questions, proteas will reveal many more truths to us in the future.

ABOVE: *Protea cynaroides* by Marianne North, 1882.

[1713]

PROTEA FORMOSA. CROWN-FLOWERED
PROTEA.

****

Clafs and Order.

TETRANDRIA MONOGYNIA.

Generic Character.

Petala 4, quorum 3 fuperne cohærentia. *Antheræ* apicibus
concavis corollæ immerfæ. *Nux* fupera undique barbata, ftylo
perfiftente coronata. BROWN.

Specific Character and Synonyms.

PROTEA *formofa ;* foliis oblongo-ellipticis marginatis, involucri bracteis fpathulatis externe fericeis, corollis tomentofis,
ftylo apice curvato, ftigmate apice incraffato.
PROTEA *formofa ;* foliis angufto-oblongis venofis obliquis:
bafi fimplici ; marginibus ramifque tomentofis, involucri
bracteis ciliatis: intimis lingulatis imberbibus, corollis arif-
tifque tomentofis, ftylo glabro apice curvato, ftigmate
apice incraffato. *Brown in Linn. Soc. Tranfact. v.* 10. *p.* 79.
Hort. Kew. ed. alt. 1. *p.* 189.
PROTEA *coronata. Bot. Repof.* 469.
ERODENDRUM *formofum ;* foliis ellipticis margine craffo,
tenellis tomentofis: bracteis involucri fimbriatis, inferioribus inter fe liberis: corolla extus tomentofa, apice valde
attenuata: antheris perangustis: ftigmatis apice craffo. *Parad.
Lond.* 76.

Our drawing of this beautiful Protea was taken at Meffrs.
LEE and KENNEDY'S, Hammerfmith, where there are varieties
with red, white, and bluifh flowers. Flowers in May. Native
of the Cape of Good-Hope, growing in the mountains of Hot-
tentots-Holland, from whence it was introduced in 1789, by
Mr. FRANCIS MASSON.

Article from *Curtis's Botanical Magazine*, 1815

This description of *Protea formosa* from *Curtis's Botanical Magazine*
describes varieties available at the nurseries of Messrs Lee and Kennedy
in Hammersmith, west London. The longest-running botanical
magazine, it was founded by William Curtis in 1787 (as *The Botanical
Magazine*) to provide "a work in which botany and gardening, or the
labours of Linnaeus or Miller, might happily be combined". In 1773
Curtis, a trained apothecary, was appointed *Praefectus Horti* and
demonstrator at the Apothecaries' garden in Chelsea, now known as
the Chelsea Physic Garden. After his death in 1799 the editor's role
was taken by Dr John Stone. He brought a more scientific approach to
the magazine, which became known as *Curtis's Botanical Magazine*.

In 1921 the Royal Horticultural Society acquired the copyright of
the struggling periodical, but connections with Kew Gardens remained
strong. The plates were hand-coloured until 1948, with colour printing
only being introduced in 1949. After a decade under the title of *The
Kew Magazine*, the journal returned to its former name in 1994, with
Christabel King as the main botanical artist. It is still published by
the Royal Botanic Gardens, Kew, under current editor Martyn Rix.
Affectionately known as the "Bot. Mag.", it is a unique resource for
those interested in horticulture, ecology or botanical illustration.

31 *Protea speciosa* with golden-
breasted cuckoo by Marianne
North, 1882.

RHODODENDRUM ARGENTEUM Hook. fil.

THE SECRET PLANTS OF SIKKIM
RHODODENDRON

VIRGINIA MILLS

In 1850 the Annual Report of the Royal Botanic Gardens, Kew recorded receipt of "21 baskets of Indian orchids and new species of *Rhododendron*" – sent from the heights of the unexplored Himalaya by Joseph Dalton Hooker. The son of Kew's first Director, Sir William Jackson Hooker, Joseph had been despatched to India by his father three years before, on a mission to collect new and notable plants for the flowerbeds and glasshouses of Kew.

Between 1848 and 1851, Joseph and his local assistants collected over 700 species, including many previously unknown to science. Of particular note were 25 new species of the genus *Rhododendron*, chiefly from the Himalayan region of Sikkim – a botanist's paradise, with rhododendrons the crowning glory. Hooker, the first European granted entry to Sikkim, vividly described it in his expedition letters, now in Kew's archive: "I get on average, 10 new plants every day; & the number still just sprouting is inconceivable. The splendour of the Rhododendrons is marvellous: there are 10 kinds on this hill, scarlet, white, lilac, yellow, pink, maroon [*sic*]: the cliffs actually bloom with them."

The genus *Rhododendron* is extraordinarily diverse, comprising more than 1,000 species of shrub and small tree. The species are prized by cultivators and gardeners variously for their large clusters of flowers, evergreen foliage and size: *Rhododendron falconeri* trees, for example, can grow to more than 15 m (49 ft). One particular species of *Rhododendron* presented a unique collecting challenge: *R. setosum*, the beautiful, purple-flowered dwarf species, has such a powerful resinous scent that it causes headaches. Its effects are compounded in the rarefied air of the high-altitude passes of the eastern Himalaya, where it is most abundant, and its dizzying effects are often confused with altitude sickness. Diluted and enjoyed at lower elevations, its scent has traditionally been used for the production of incense.

Rhododendron seed season coincides in Sikkim with the pre-monsoon rains, conspiring with perilous terrain – "certainly one often progresses spread-eagle fashion against the cliff, for some distance, & crosses narrow planks over profound Abysses, with no hand-hold whatever" – to make Hooker's travels dangerous and uncomfortable. Not surprisingly, his letters sometimes give vent to frustration: "Alas one of my finest collections of Rhododendron sent today got

OPPOSITE: *Rhododendron dalhousieae* by Walter Hood Fitch, from J. D. Hooker: *The Rhododendrons of the Sikkim-Himalaya*, 1849.

ABOVE: Idealized portrait of Joseph Dalton Hooker by William Tayler during his Himalayan travels, *c.*1850.

ruined … so I have to collect the troublesome things afresh. If your shins were as bruised as mine with tearing through the interminable Rhod[odendron]. scrub of 10–13,000 ft. you would be as sick of the sight of these glories as I am."

Hooker also fell foul of political obstacles. With relations between British India, Sikkim and neighbouring Tibet highly sensitive, he had been given strict instructions not to cross the Sikkim–Tibet border. But the lure of more unexplored country proved impossible to resist, resulting in his arrest and imprisonment in November 1849 by the Rajah of Sikkim.

Word of Hooker's internment spread quickly to the ears of Lord Dalhousie, the Governor of British India. Lady Dalhousie had recently been honoured by Hooker's naming one of his finest new rhododendrons, with exceptionally large and sweet-smelling blooms, after her. Perhaps this flattering association helped to persuade Lord Dalhousie to secure Hooker's release. He threatened military invasion of Sikkim unless the prisoner was set free, and the Rajah was forced to cede to his demands.

Hooker and his plant collections returned safely to Kew Gardens, where the rhododendrons were cultivated. His book, *The Rhododendrons of the Sikkim–Himalaya*, published in 1849–51, was spectacularly illustrated by Walter Hood Fitch, drawing upon Hooker's own field sketches and specimens. It created a craze for the showy blooms in gardens across Europe, and secured Hooker's enduring association with the genus *Rhododendron*. During his lifetime, a Chinese species was named *R. hookeri* in his honour.

LEFT: *Rhododendron dalhousiae* by Walter Hood Fitch from J. D. Hooker: *The Rhododendrons of the Sikkim–Himalaya*, 1849–51.

Tab. I.

RHODODENDRON DALHOUSIAE, Hook. fil.
(in its native locality)

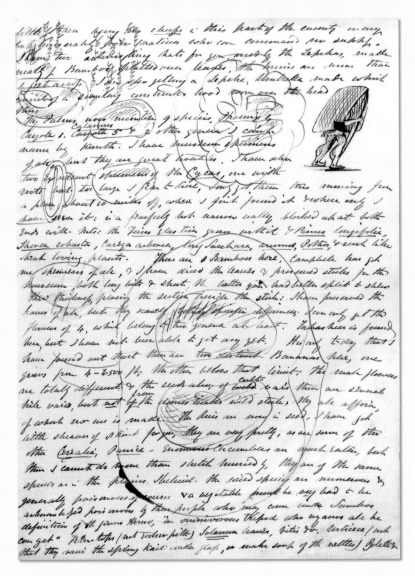

Letter from Joseph Dalton Hooker to his father, from Darjeeling, Sikkim-Himalaya, 30 August 1848

The Kew archive contains thousands of letters written by Joseph Hooker, documenting his botanical expeditions and tenure as Director of the Gardens. This extract was written to his father, William, during Joseph's Himalayan expedition. It features a marginal illustration of an "umbrella hood", used by the Lepcha people as protection from the daily rains. During his time in India and the Himalayas, Hooker was keen to employ local people such as the Lepchas to help him collect plants. He saw the advantage of their local knowledge not only for locating where plants of interest grew but to show him the ways they used plant materials in their everyday lives. The type of umbrella illustrated was made by plaiting bamboo over leaves. Though Hooker doesn't say whether he ever wore one himself for relief from the weather which made his plant hunting so arduous, he did purchase many such everyday plant items. He sent the objects back to his father at Kew Gardens, where they were put on display in the Economic Botany Museum and many remain in the collection to this day.

32 *Rhododendron hookeri* by Walter Hood Fitch, from *Curtis's Botanical Magazine*, 1856.

Rosa damascena
Blush Damask Rose

GLAMOUR FROM ANOTHER AGE
DAMASK ROSE

MARTYN RIX

The words "damask rose" conjure up visions of the scented palaces of Ottoman Istanbul, sprinkled with rosewater and containing bowls of rose-flavoured pink *lokum* (Turkish delight). Attar of roses is a dense oil, made by the distillation of hundreds of thousands of damask rose flowers: a thin film of the precious oil is formed on the surface of the rosewater which condenses from the still. This very valuable oil is now produced in Turkey, around the city of Isparta in western Anatolia, by families who were relocated from Bulgaria in approximately 1920 following the break-up of the Ottoman Empire. Kazanluk in central Bulgaria, east of Sofia, remains an important centre of this production, and the rose used to produce this oil goes by many names: "Trigintipetala" ("thirty-petalled") is the oldest name, but it is also called "Kazanlik". Other names are "Summer Damask" or "Rose à parfum de Grasse", referring to the French town that is still the centre of the perfume trade.

The volcanic hills around Isparta are terraced and planted with hedges of roses, which flower in May; the pale pink buds are picked by hand before the sun rises, just as they are opening, and sent to the distilleries for the extraction of the oil. "Trigintipetala" is the clone most often used for scent production, though others are grown elsewhere – notably forms of the white *R. × alba*, which thrives in colder climates.

As a group of garden roses, the damasks are some of the oldest known. They were grown by the Romans across the empire (Paestum was famous for its roses) and are said to have been used in the cult of the goddess Hera at the Heraion on the island of Samos.

The origin of damask roses is obscure, but they are probably hybrids between the low-growing, often red-flowered *R. gallica* and the climbing, white-flowered musk rose *R. moschata*, or some other white-flowered rose from Asia. Most damask roses are pink and flower only in summer, but some, for example "Mme Hardy", have pure white flowers and others, such as "Semperflorens" or the "Autumn Damask", have a second flowering in early autumn. Most are double-flowered, but "Hebe's Lip" is a single white rose with a narrow deep-red edge.

During the great fashion for roses in 19th-century France, damask roses were crossed with other species. "Blush Damask" is probably a hybrid with *R. pimpinellifolia*, and "La Ville de Bruxelles", a particularly

OPPOSITE: *Rosa x damascena* by Mary Lawrance, from M. Lawrance: *A Collection of Roses from Nature*, 1799.

ABOVE: *Rosa indica* by Pierre Joseph Redouté, from P. J. Redouté: *Choix des plus belles fleurs et des plus beaux fruits*, 1833.

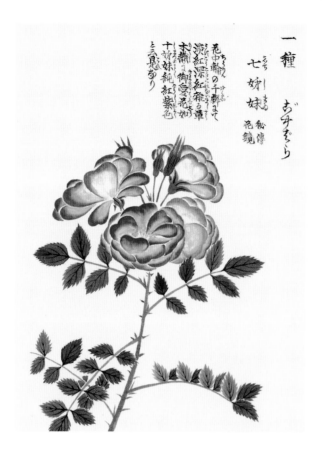

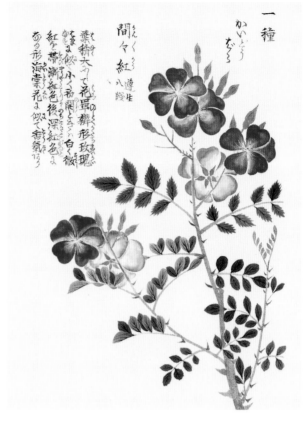

fine double pink, is perhaps a cross with *R. × alba*. Further confusion arises because the double-flowered red *R. gallica* "Officinalis" or "Rose of Provins", another rose grown by the Romans and shown on wall paintings in Heracleum, is often called the red damask. The plant is said by tradition to have been brought from Damascus to France in the 13th century by Thibault IV, Le Chansonnier; it was much cultivated around Provins for medicinal and culinary use. A famous miniature in the Topkapi Palace Museum in Istanbul shows Sultan Mehmet II (1432–81), known as "the Conqueror", delicately holding red rosebuds to his nose.

Damask roses are easy to grow, but are best in dry, warm, sunny climates. The plants should be pruned by removing the old flowering shoots immediately after the flowers have faded, and the bushes can be cut hard back every third year (again after flowering) to rejuvenate the plants.

ABOVE: Roses by Kan'en Iwasaki, from *Honzu Zufu*, 1828.

LEFT: Roses from R. J. Thornton: *New Illustration of the Sexual System of Carolus von Linnaeus and the Temple of Flora, or Garden of Nature*, 1807.

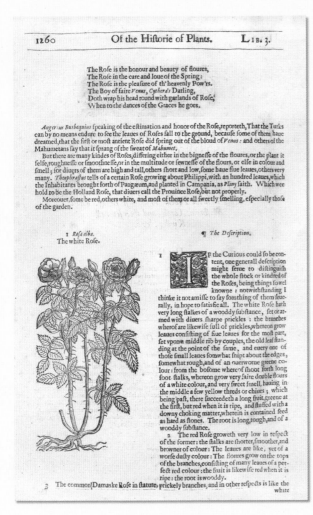
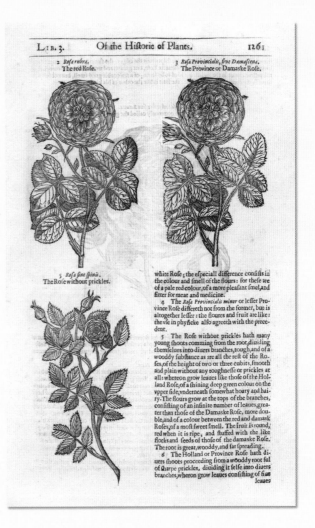

Pages from Gerard's herbal or *The Historie of Plants*, 1597

Gerard's herbal, or *The Historie of Plants*, was first published in 1597, at a time when Elizabeth I was on the throne of England and William Shakespeare was writing plays.

Gerard lived in London, and was a keen gardener, managing the gardens of his patron, Lord Burghley, in the Strand while tending his own garden in Holborn. His herbal was based on earlier works published in Latin, but he added his own observations and thoughts, as well as popular English names and instructions on how to prepare the herbs and vegetables.

The second page from *The Historie of Plants* shown here features illustrations of three cultivated roses: no. 2, the red Rose, is probably *Rosa gallica* "Officinalis"; no. 3, the province or Damaske rose, is probably our "Trigintipetala", the damask; and no. 5, the rose without prickles, is probably the double form of *Rosa majalis*, the Cinnamon rose from eastern Europe – the suckering, almost thornless stems and round hips, noted by Gerard, are characteristic of this species.

33 *Rosa gallica* by Pancrace Bessa, from H. L. Duhamel du Monceau: *Traité des arbres et arbustes*, Nouvelle édition, 1819.

FROM FOUL SMELLS TO INNER STARS
STAPELIA

DAVID GOYDER

Fleshy, succulent stems provide a valuable way of storing water in arid environments and have evolved in many different groups of plants. In some plants, photosynthesis, the chemical reaction that produces nutrients when the plant is exposed to sunlight, also takes place in the stem. Leaves are greatly reduced in size, often appearing in modified form as scales or spines.

Cacti, perhaps the best-known plants to have adopted this strategy, are a striking feature of the landscape and vegetation in drier parts of the Americas. In Africa, cacti are replaced by members of other plant families, in particular *Euphorbia* (Euphorbiaceae) and the stapeliads (Apocynaceae), as shown here. The stapeliads are a group of nearly 350 species of plants with succulent stems and extraordinarily diverse, complex and often beautiful flowers. They can be found in drier parts of southern Africa, the horn of Africa, the Arabian Peninsula and India. Although related to the periwinkle, the flowers look very different. Flowers in this family have evolved along with the bees, butterflies, wasps, flies or even birds that pollinate them to produce some very bizarre forms. This is very similar to the orchid family, which is not at all closely related. Orchid flowers and pollinators have also evolved in parallel to give a huge range of shapes, colours and forms.

Stapelia hirsuta employs large blowflies to transfer its pollen. It attracts the flies using a foul smell, fooling the insect into thinking that the flower is a piece of rotting flesh – perfect to lay its eggs in. The brown or purple colours of the flower, as well as its wrinkled, hairy surface, are all part of the deception. The fly moves around the flower, looking for somewhere to lay its eggs and to feed on nectar, which is held in the centre of the flower. The rigid, star-like structure limits the angle at which the insect can approach the centre. One of its legs or its proboscis is guided into one of five grooves around this star. Pollen lies at the top of this groove, and this becomes attached to the fly's leg or proboscis as it frees itself.

Stapeliads and orchids are very unusual plants as their pollen comes in packages, not individual grains. Pollen grains are glued together to form what are called pollinia. In *Stapelia*, these pollinia occur in pairs, which are transported as a unit from flower to flower by visiting pollinators. So when the fly moves to another flower to feed on the nectar in its centre, the pollinia it is carrying get stuck in one of the

OPPOSITE: *Stapelia vetula* (now regarded as a variety of *S. hirsuta*) from, F. Masson: *Stapeliae Novae*, 1797.

ABOVE: *Stapelia maculosa*, from *Curtis's Botanical Magazine*, 1833.

grooves of the second flower, and the fly has unwittingly pollinated the *Stapelia*!

The succulent stem is not the only way in which stapeliads adapt to the dry conditions. Their system of transferring pollen is another, as each individual pollinium, or pollen mass, is encased in a waxy coating that prevents it from drying out. This may be the key innovation that has enabled plants of this fascinating family to exploit desert and seasonally dry habitats. Indeed, Kew researchers have presented evidence that links such floral innovations to changes in Africa's climate around 20 million years ago and the rapid diversification of this group of plants across the continent around that time.

RIGHT: *Stapelia hirsuta* by N. E. Brown, watercolour and pencil on paper, *c.*1880.

BELOW: *A South African Speciality* by Marianne North, 1882.

Expences at the Cape of Good Hope
account of His Britannic Majesty, from
the first of March 1788 to the first of Jan.y
1788 Including a Journey to the Elephant
River being about 200 miles dist from the Cape

To two Journies to False Bay	20 _ 6
To Boat hire on various occasions	14 _ 7
To Cooley hire on various occasions	22 . 1
To Garden Pots & Boxes	75 _ 7
To Stationary Ware	22
To a large Chest	12
To Baskets	7 _ _
To a large Carr	220
To 10 Oxen à 12 R.D. each	120
To a Dutch Waggoner & Hottentot for 5 months à 15 R.D: p.r month	75
To Powder & Shot	12 _ 6
To Cooking Utensils	20 7
To various necefsaries for the Journey	45 6
To 10 Months Board & lodging	40 0
	1069 u

List of expenses for the items Francis Masson took on an expedition to South Africa in 1788-89

Francis Masson was Joseph Banks's plant collector in South Africa and accompanied James Cook's second expedition to the Cape of Good Hope. By 1775, after nearly three years there, Masson had sent back over 500 plant species to England. He travelled extensively to the Cape of Good Hope, spending 12 years there in total. During this time he published his only book, *Stapelia Novae: or a collection of several new species of that genus discovered in the interior parts of Africa*, engraved from sketches made by Masson. He also travelled widely in northern Africa, the West Indies and North America.

This list of expenses by Masson from the Cape of Good Hope covers the period 1788–89. This includes two journeys to False Bay, one of the main areas of plant collecting, as well as for items such as "powder shot" and "cooking utensils".

34 *Stapelia hamata* by Miss Westcombe, watercolour on paper, mid-19th century.

KEW'S GLORIOUS "BIRD OF PARADISE"
STRELITZIA

JOANNE YEOMANS

Indigenous to South Africa, the five known species of *Strelitzia*, from the Strelitziaceae family, include the magnificent *Strelitzia reginae* – commonly known as the bird of paradise or crane flower. In the right conditions the plant can flower all year round, and its popular orange and blue flowers are often used in floristry due to their ornamental quality. *Strelitzia reginae* is a bold, structural plant that grows up to 2 m (6 ft 6 in) and supports the weight of pollinating sunbirds and weaverbirds. The birds are attracted to the brightly coloured petals, and pollen sticks to their bodies or feet when they are drinking the plant's nectar. The Victorian artist Marianne North visited South Africa in 1882–3, having decided that her gallery at Kew represented "all the continents of the world … except Africa, and [she] resolved to begin painting there without loss of time". She spent nine months in South Africa, completing over 100 paintings, and her painting of *S. reginae* includes a sunbird pollinating the flower (see opposite).

Strelitzia reginae was discovered and brought back to England by Kew's first plant collector, Francis Masson. A Scottish botanist, Masson came to Kew in the 1760s and worked as an under gardener before being selected by Sir Joseph Banks to travel to South Africa with Captain Cook on HMS *Resolution*. They sailed in 1772, and Masson stayed in South Africa until 1775. He returned to England having sent back more than 500 newly discovered species; one of these, the *Strelitzia reginae*, was introduced at Kew in 1773. Sir Joseph Banks named the newly discovered genus *Strelitzia* after Queen Charlotte, the wife of George III, who was born Princess Sophie Charlotte of Mecklenburg-Strelitz. The specific Latin name *reginae* means "of the queen", and also respects Charlotte's interest in botany. She had her own collection of living specimens at Windsor Castle and, along with pressing flowers, enjoyed lectures on zoology and botany from the President of the newly formed Linnaean Society, Sir James Edward Smith.

The arrival of exotic plants such as *S. reginae* in England would have been extraordinary for the botanists at Kew. The plant was featured in *Curtis's Botanical Magazine* in 1791; it described *S. reginae* as "one of the most scarce and magnificent plants introduced" into Britain and noted that it was "something uncommonly beautiful".

After the death of Princess Augusta, the Dowager Princess of Wales, in 1772, Banks was keen to develop Kew from a private royal residence

OPPOSITE: *Strelitzia and Sugar Birds, South Africa* by Marianne North, 1882.

ABOVE: *Strelitzia reginae* by Franz Bauer, from F. Bauer: *Strelitzia depicta, or coloured figures of the known species of the genus Strelitzia from the drawings in the Banksian library*, 1818.

LEFT: *Strelitzia augusta* by Franz Bauer, from F. Bauer: *Strelitzia depicta, or coloured figures of the known species of the genus Strelitzia from the drawings in the Banksian library*, 1818.

into a global centre for plant transfer between collectors and colonial botanical gardens. Creating an unofficial role for himself at Kew, he enjoyed the support and patronage of George III. He commissioned plant-collecting trips and amassed large collections of living plants, as well as dried specimens and seeds. He sought to bring as many newly discovered species as possible to Kew, in order to compete with other historic botanical gardens in Europe, such as Paris and Vienna. Banks decided to concentrate on practical horticulture and focused collecting, rather than the disorganized acquisitioning of Princess Augusta's time. In 1768, the botanist John Hill published *Hortus Kewensis*, detailing the 3,400 species in Princess Augusta's garden. William Aiton published an updated version with the same title in 1789, revealing that under Banks's successful direction the number of species at Kew had increased to 5,600. A second edition of Aiton's book, in 1810–13, featured more new species, including approximately 300 from Australia, 120 from China and 220 from Siberia, taking the total number of species at Kew

to 11,000. Banks also encouraged botanists to use his vast herbarium to identify new species and he employed the botanical artist Franz Bauer as "Botanick Painter to the King", despite Banks paying the salary himself. Banks believed that a botanical garden such as Kew needed a painter in order to record its living collections, as plants flowered in the gardens.

Born in 1758, Franz Bauer was a botanical artist in Vienna before coming to England in 1788. He gave drawing lessons to the daughters of George III and Queen Charlotte, which included colouring Bauer's "Erica" engravings. He published *Strelitzia depicta: or coloured figures of the known species of the genus Strelitzia from the drawings in the Banksian library* in 1818, showing detailed lithographs of the known species of *Strelitzia* from plants likely to have been grown at Kew. This slim volume was probably hand-coloured by Bauer, and its prints display the detail and delicacy of the original paintings. Bauer spent the rest of his life at Kew. He died there in 1840 and is buried at St Anne's Church, Kew.

PENTANDRIA MONOGYNIA.   28*5*

STRELITZIA.

Spathæ. *Cal.* o. *Cor.* 3-petala. *Nectar.* 3-phyllum,
genitalia involvens. *Peric.* 3-loculare, polyfper-
mum.

1. STRELITZIA. TAB. 2.   *Reginæ.*
Heliconia Bihai. *J. Mill. ic. tab.* 5, 6.
Canna-leav'd Strelitzia.
Nat. of the Cape of Good Hope.
Introd. 1773, by Sir Joſeph Banks, Bart.
Fl. April and May.   S. ♄.
DESCR. *Folia* omnia radicalia, petiolata, oblonga,
integerrima, margine inferne undulato crifpo, gla-
berrima, ſubtus glaucefcentia, coriacea, pedalia,
perfiſtentia. *Petioli* ſubcompreſſi, tripedales et ul-
tra, craſſitie pollicis, vaginantes, erecti,   ᵇrἰ.
Scapus longitudine et craſſitie petiolorum, erectus,
teres, tectus *vaginis* alternis, remotis, acuminatis,
viridibus margine purpuraſcente. *Spatha* univer-
ſalis ſpithamæ, extus viridis, margine purpuraſ-
cens; ſpathæ partiales albidæ. *Petala* lutea, qua-
driuncialia. *Nectarium* cæruleum.
OBS. Differentia ſpecifica Heliconiæ albæ in *Linn.
fuppl.* 157. hujus eſt plantæ, ſed nomen triviale ad
aliam pertinet ſpeciem Africanam, in hortis Euro-
pæis nondum obviam.

ACHYRANTHES. *Gen. pl.* 288.

Cal. 5-phyllus. *Cor.* o. *Stigma* 2-fidum. *Semina*
folitaria.

1. A. caule fruticoſo erecto, calycibus reflexis ſpicæ ad-   *aſpera.*
preſſis. *Syſt. veget.* 246.

α Amaran-

Description of *Strelitzia reginae* from *Hortus Kewensis*, 1789

Hortus Kewensis or *A catalogue of the plants cultivated in the Royal Botanic Garden at Kew* was produced in three volumes by William Aiton in 1789 as an updated version to the original by John Hill. Aiton was chief gardener at Kew and was succeeded by his son William Townsend Aiton, who published a second edition in 1810–13.

In this entry, Joseph Banks is credited with the introduction of *Strelitzia reginae* from the Cape of Good Hope; however, it was Francis Masson who brought the first live specimen back to England.

At the beginning of his three-volume work, Aiton dedicates his publication to King George III:

"To the King. Permit, Sir, a servant rendered happy by Your Majesty's benevolence, to obey the impulse of gratitude, which urges him to lay at Your Majesty's feet, this attempt to make public the present state of the Royal Botanic Garden at Kew."

35 *Strelitzia reginae* by Franz Bauer, from F. Bauer: *Strelitzia depicta, or coloured figures of the known species of the genus Strelitzia from the drawings in the Banksian library*, 1818.

FATAL ATTRACTION:
THE "CORPSE FLOWER" OF KEW
AMORPHOPHALLUS TITANUM

LYNN PARKER

*A*morphophallus titanum was discovered in the central Sumatran rainforest in 1878 by the Italian naturalist Dr Odoardo Beccari. He heralded it as a "giant among flowers", superseding even the great *Rafflesia arnoldii* – news which aroused both scepticism and astonishment in European scientific circles. *The Gardeners' Chronicle*, reporting on the discovery in December 1878, announced that several tubers and seeds had "safely arrived in Florence and look quite healthy and sound", prudently adding: "On looking at fossil remains of plants and animals we are often disposed to say, 'Verily, there were giants in those days,' but Sumatra may still boast of giants still in existence." Beccari was most effusive regarding the size of his find: "a man standing upright can barely reach the top of the spadix with his hand … and with open arms he can scarcely reach half way round the circumference of the funnel-shaped spathe from the bottom of which the spadix arises."

Beccari did not exaggerate the plant's dimensions. The flowers, growing to more than 3 m (10 ft), cluster upon a stem to form what is more accurately described as an inflorescence. This fragrant spadix of flowers is enveloped in what resembles a large petal, with a deep green outer surface and a dark claret red on the interior, known as a spath. When the flowers are ready for pollination, the tip of the spadix heats up to a maximum of 36–38°C (96.8–100.4°F) in a process known as thermogenesis. The plant then emits a powerful and nauseating smell resembling rotting meat, produced to attract the plant's pollinator, most commonly carrion flies, beetles or tiny sweat bees, so called as they are often attracted to perspiration. The plant's heat, smell and colour combine to attract insects by its similarity to decaying flesh – so unpleasant that *A. titanum* is known in Indonesia as the "corpse flower". The name "titan arum" was first used by the broadcaster Sir David Attenborough while making his television series *The Private Life of Plants* for the BBC; he considered that repeatedly referring to *Amorphophallus* would be absurd.

After graduating, Odoardo Beccari spent several months at Kew, where he became acquainted with William and Joseph Hooker and Charles Darwin. During this time, he met perhaps his most important associate, James Brooke, which led to Beccari's subsequent exploration of Sarawak (part of the island of Borneo), culminating in his discovery of *A. titanum*. At the botanic garden in Florence, several young plants germinated from the seeds that Beccari dispatched to his patron, the Marquis Bardo Corsi Salviati, and it was only natural that one seedling should be sent to Kew.

When *A. titanum* first flowered at Kew in 1889, some ten years later, it caused a sensation, exciting great public interest. The plant emitted a rancid odour, said to resemble "a mixture of rotten fish and burnt sugar" as it flowered, attracting "many blue-bottle flies". Visitors were greatly disturbed by the smell. The artist Matilda Smith, who recorded this first flowering for the *Botanical Magazine*, endured many hours painting it, eventually falling ill. Joseph Hooker, Kew's incumbent Director, acknowledged a "deep obligation" to Miss Smith, "who, in her efforts to do justice by her pencil to these plants, suffered in each case a prolonged martyrdom". In 1926, when the plant flowered again, police were called to control the vast crowds.

The titan arum remains a very challenging plant to cultivate. Even under the best possible conditions, it still takes approximately six years to flower from seed. Since 2005, there have been several flowerings each year at Kew, thanks to the experience and expertise of the staff.

OPPOSITE: *Amorphophallus titanum* in bloom in the Waterlily House at Kew, 1920s.

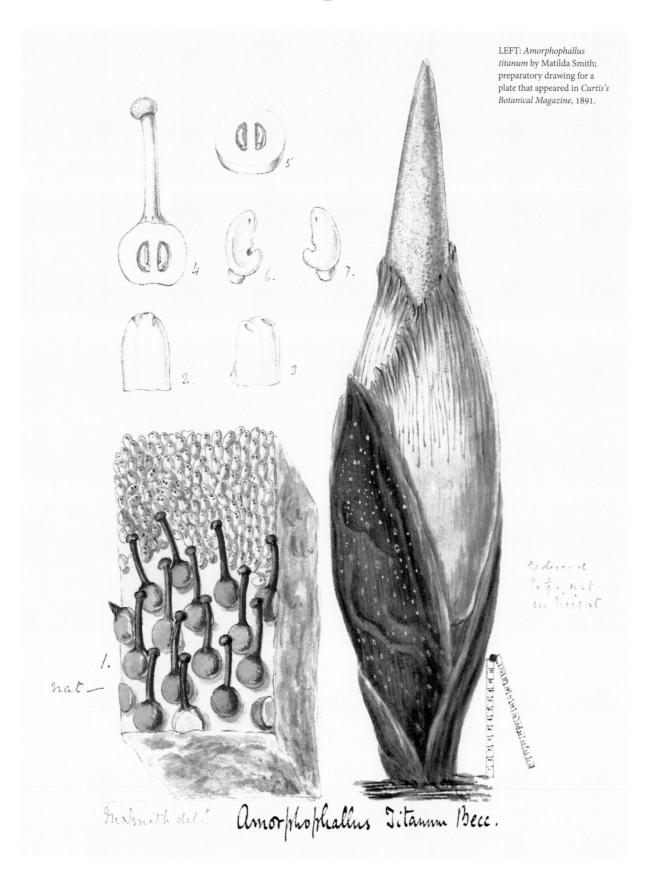

LEFT: *Amorphophallus titanum* by Matilda Smith; preparatory drawing for a plate that appeared in *Curtis's Botanical Magazine*, 1891.

TAB. 7153, 4, 5.

AMORPHOPHALLUS TITANUM.

Native of Sumatra.

Nat. Ord. AROIDEÆ.—Tribe PYTHONIEÆ.

Genus AMORPHOPHALLUS, *Blume*; (*Benth. et Hook. f. Gen. Pl.* vol. iii. p. 971.)

AMORPHOPHALLUS (Brachyspatha) *Titanum*; tubere maximo depresso-globoso, folii petiolo 16-pedali lævi albo-punctato, lamina ambitu 30–45-pedali trisecta, segmentis di-tri-sectis dichotome pinnatisectis pinnatifidisectisve ultimis ovato-oblongis caudato-acuminatis, sinubus angustissimis, supra læte viridibus nervis impressis subtus pallidioribus, pedunculo brevi crasso albo-punctato, spatha juniore cataphyllis oblongis luride viridibus albo punctatis vestita, maturæ tubo crasso infundibulari-flavo virescente in laminam late campanulatam rubro-purpuream expanso, lamina 3–4 ped. diam. ambitu recurva plicata marginibus grosse inæqualiter dentatis, spadice spatha sub duplo longiore 5-pedali crasso stricto erecto, appendice quam inflorescentia triplo longiore a basi ad apicem sensim attenuato pallide aureo-flavo lævi, inflorescentiis tubo spathæ inclusis 10 poll. diam., femineis e ovariis globosis sessilibus dissitis 2–3-locularibus in stylos duplo longiores contractis, stigmatibus globosis, loculis 1-ovulatis, ovulis basilaribus infl. masc. e antheris sessilibus confertis ellipsoideis 2-porosis, baccis ovoideis rubris 1–2-spermis, seminibus plano-convexis.

A. *Titanum*, *Beccari in Bull. Soc. Toscan. di Ortic.* 1879, p. 46 ; *Arcangeli in Nuov. Giorn. Bot. Ital.* vol. xi. (1879), p. 217 ; *Engler, Monog. Arac.* p. 643 ; *Masters in Gard. Chron.* 1886. ii. p. 432, figs. 88 and 89 ; 1889, i. p. 746 and 804, figs. 119 and 120 ; 1889, ii. 19, figs. 3, 5, 6 ; *Beccari in Bull. Soc. Toscan. di Ortic.* Ser. 2, vol. iv. 1889, p. 250, 266, t. viii. et *Schneider in Le Jardin.* 1889, p. 178. (*cum Ic. ex Journ. Hort.* vol. lxxxii. p. 6, f. 2, iterat.)

Conophallus Titanum, *Beccari in Bull. Soc. Tosc. di Ortic.* 1878, p. 271, 291 ; *Masters in Gard. Chron.* 1878, p. 788, fig. 127.

The earliest account of this wonderful plant that reached Europe, is contained in an article under the title " Una Pianta Maravigliosa," communicated by Signor Fenzi of Florence, to the Royal Tuscan Society of Horticulture, in September, 1878 (Bull. Soc. Toscan. di Ortic. 1878, p. 271). It consists of the contents of a letter addressed from Sumatra by the illustrious traveller and botanist, Dr. Beccari, to his friend the Marchese Corsi Salviati, in which he announces the discovery of a gigantic aroid, probably belonging to the genus *Conophallus*, and gives some details of its huge dimensions. It was shortly afterwards followed by another article under the title of

JANUARY 1ST, 1891.

Conophallus ? Titanum in the same Journal, p. 290, and from the same sources, giving fuller details as to its fruiting condition and foliage, together with a sketch of the plant in its flowering state. Together with this information Dr. Beccari sent both tubers and seeds to the Marchese. As regards the tubers the result was unfortunate ; for, according to the law of 1875, making provision against the introduction of the vine disease (*Phyllorera*), the tubers were detained at Marseilles till they rotted. The seeds, on the other hand, arrived in good condition, and germinated in the Marchese's garden, whence some very young plants were transmitted to Kew by that nobleman, at Dr. Beccari's request.

In 1878 the accounts received from Dr. Beccari were communicated by Signor Fenzi to the " Gardener's Chronicle," published in December of the same year (vol. 1878, ii. pp. 596 and 788), together with a copy of the sketch of the flowering plant.

In the following year a full botanical account of the plant was drawn up from Dr. Beccari's notes by Prof. Arcangeli, which appeared in the new Journal of the Botanical Society of Italy (vol. xi. p. 217) under the title of " L'Amorphophallus Titanum, *Beccari*, illustrato di G. Arcangeli " (*Conophallus* being regarded by botanists as a section of the latter genus). Before proceeding further with the history of this bulky vegetable I shall give Dr. Beccari's account of its discovery, extracted from his article in the Bulletin of the Royal Tuscan Society of Horticulture, vol. iv. (1889), p. 250, with a figure copied by permission of Dr. Hogg from the Journal of Horticulture.

" It was on the 6th of August, 1878, at Ajer Mantcior, in the Padang Province of Sumatra, that I found the leaves of this extraordinary plant. Shortly afterwards, being at Kajù Tanam, a place not far from Ajer Mantcior, and there informed that the *Amorphophallus* was common on the surrounding hills, I offered a large reward to any one who would bring me a flower. This promise produced a more speedy effect than I could have hoped for, for on the 5th of September, towards midday, I had the satisfaction of possessing a flower of this marvel.

" The single flower (or more correctly inflorescence) with

Article from *Curtis's Botanical Magazine*, 1891

This description of *Amorphophallus titanum* is from *Curtis's Botanical Magazine*, 1 January 1891. The article refers the reader to Beccari's account of his discovery, described as a "wonderful plant" and a "gigantic aroid". The editor of the magazine was Sir Joseph Dalton Hooker (1817–1911), then director of the Royal Botanic Gardens at Kew; he had taken over the role from his father, Sir William Jackson Hooker, in 1865.

Joseph Hooker, a celebrated botanist and explorer, studied medicine at Glasgow University before undertaking an expedition to the Antarctic, led by James Clark Ross. Between 1847 and 1851 he travelled in the Himalayas, and later visited Palestine, Morocco and the United States. Hooker became a close friend of Charles Darwin and was elected a fellow of the Royal Society, serving as its president in 1873–77. He published numerous scientific papers and monographs including *Flora of British India*, *The Student's Flora of the British Isles* and the vast *Genera Plantarum*, a collaboration with George Bentham based on the collections at Kew. Another of Hooker's works, *Handbook of the British Flora*, begun by Bentham and completed by Hooker, remained a standard text for the next hundred years.

36 *Amorphophallus titanum* by Matilda Smith, from *Curtis's Botanical Magazine*, 1891.

$\times \frac{1}{3}$

THE PLANT THAT
SPARKED A FLOWER FRENZY
TULIPA

RICHARD WILFORD

In colourful drifts through parks and gardens, bursting out of pots and window boxes and scattered through spring borders, the tulip is as popular now as it has ever been. Tulips have been cultivated in Europe for more than 450 years; long before that they were revered in Turkey, where flowers with extremely narrow, pointed petals, known as "needle tulips", were favoured. In the cities of the Ottoman Empire, especially Istanbul (formerly Constantinople), tulips were planted in palace gardens and depicted on decorative tiles. By the 16th century, tulips were flourishing in Ottoman horticulture, and from there they inevitably found their way to Europe.

The tulip was virtually unknown in European horticulture when the Swiss physician and naturalist Conrad Gesner published an illustration of a cultivated tulip in his *De Hortis Germaniae* in 1561 (see overleaf). This plant was raised from seed imported from Turkey, and was seen growing in a garden in Augsberg, Germany. It had a red, bowl-shaped flower, unlike the needle tulips grown in Ottoman gardens. This suggests that it was a wild species, probably *Tulipa suaveolens*.

A few species grow naturally in Turkey and southern Europe, but the real home of the tulip is much further east, in the hills and mountains of Central Asia. On remote hillsides, from Iran to Kazakhstan, the spring blooms of tulips decorate grassy meadows, rocky slopes and sandy plains before dying back to their underground bulbs for the long, dry summer. When dormant, the bulbs are easily transported, which aided their spread to the gardens of Europe.

This mysterious eastern flower caught the imagination of naturalists and gardeners. Trade with the Ottoman Empire led to bulbs reaching other parts of Western Europe, including the Netherlands. Carolus Clusius (after whom the species *T. clusiana* is named) was a famous French botanist and foremost among the tulip enthusiasts of the time.

OPPOSITE: *Tulipa undulatifolia* by Mary Grierson, 1973. © Mary Grierson.

RIGHT: Tulip by Georg Dionysius Ehret, 1740.

He grew tulips in the Imperial Gardens of Vienna before moving to the new botanic garden at the University of Leiden in Holland in 1593. From there, he sent bulbs and seeds to growers across Europe.

To add to the mystery of this enticing flower, the colour of the blooms sometimes broke into streaks, called flames or feathers, over a pale yellow or white background. The cause of this apparently spontaneous and unpredictable "breaking" was unknown. It drove tulip growers into a frenzy of excitement and wonder, eventually leading to the infamous "tulip mania" that seized Holland in the 1630s. Then, the rarest broken tulips changed hands for huge sums of money before the market collapsed in 1637.

The cause of tulip breaking is now known to be a virus that can also distort and weaken a plant. Nevertheless, broken tulips remained popular, and it was only towards the end of the 19th century that plain flowers, often called breeders, or cottage tulips, were widely grown as ornamental plants. New introductions from Central Asia, such as *T. kaufmanniana*, *T. greigii* and *T. fosteriana*, added to the tulip breeders' stock, and even more varieties were created by crossing them with existing hybrids. Today, there are nearly 6,000 registered tulip cultivars, and the choice can be overwhelming.

What at first glance may seem a simple plant is surprisingly varied, with an intriguing history. A tulip can be a vivid bloom that dazzles in a spring garden, a delicate species adapted to growing in a hostile habitat or a mystical flower of the East. Add to this the range of flower shapes, forms and colours available today, and you can see why this beautiful plant is loved by so many.

RIGHT: *Tulipa clusiana* by Sydenham Teast Edwards, from *Curtis's Botanical Magazine*, 1811.

Extract from *De Hortis Germaniaea* by Conrad Gesner, 1561

This very early illustration of a tulip appeared in *De Hortis Germaniaea* by Conrad Gesner, published in 1561. He described the plant, which he had noticed growing in the garden of a magistrate, Johann Heinrich Herwart, in Augsberg in 1559, as being similar to "a red lily". He named it *Tulipa turcarum*, believing it to have been grown from seed from Byzantium or possibly Cappadocia (in Turkey). Tulips were just beginning to enter Europe through a variety of routes as trade in the Levant increased.

Gesner (1516–65) was a Swiss botanist, physician and classical linguist who studied in Zurich, Strasbourg and Basel. In 1537 he was appointed Professor of Greek at the newly established Academy of Lausanne, where he was also able to study botany. His notes and about 1,500 wood-engravings of plants, flowers and seeds were used by other authors for over two centuries after his death.

Gesner compiled a major zoological encyclopedia, the *Historiae animalium*, published between 1551 and 1558. The first European work to describe the brown rat and the guinea pig, it ran to four volumes and 4,500 pages, covering quadrupeds, amphibians, birds and fishes. He also published the four-volume *Bibliotheca Universalis*, intended to be a comprehensive list of Latin, Greek and Hebrew works, in 1545.

37 Tulips by Simon Verelst, early 17th century.

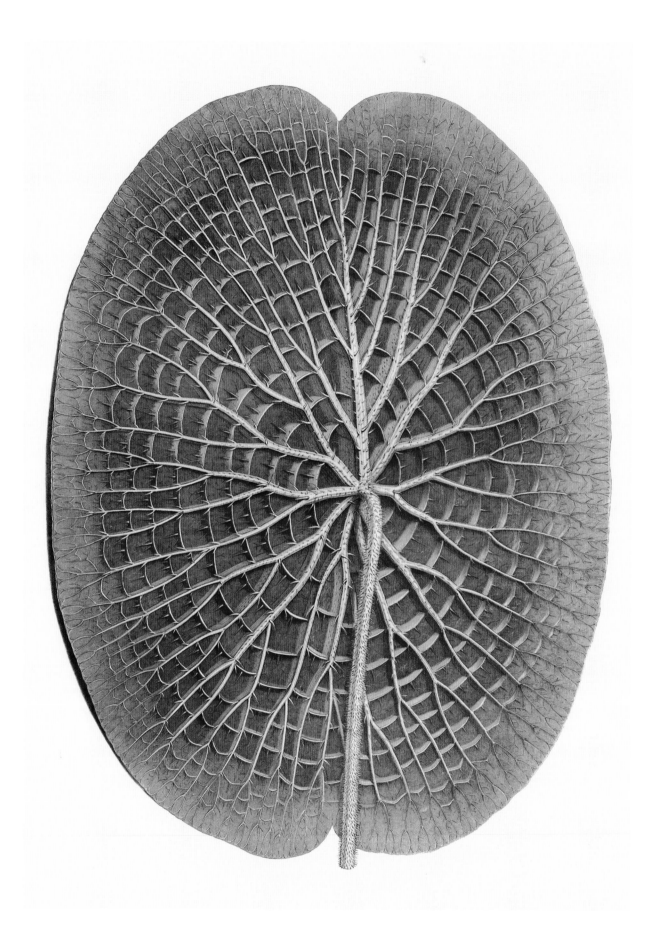

QUEEN OF THE WATERLILIES
VICTORIA AMAZONICA

GINA FULLERLOVE

"A vegetable wonder" was how the surveyor Robert Schomburgk described this behemoth of a plant when first encountered on the river Berbice in British Guiana (now Guyana). It was 1 January 1837, and Schomburgk, sent by the Royal Geographical Society to survey waterways in the interior of this newly acquired South American territory, was struggling to make headway up the river. As his crew paddled closer to the plant, he saw a huge and beautiful waterlily. It was in full bloom, and its many flowers scented the air with heady fragrance.

Schomburgk described his discovery as: "a gigantic leaf from five to six feet in diameter, salver shaped, with a broad rim of light green above and vivid crimson below, rested upon the water", and adding, "all calamities were forgotten … I felt as a Botanist, and felt myself rewarded."

The plant's enormous circular leaves can grow to over 2.5 m (8 ft) across. Their upturned rims are anchored by long stalks, arising from underground stems buried in the muddy riverbed. First appearing as spiny heads, the leaves expand rapidly – up to half a square metre per day. Their surface appears quilted, with a waxy layer that repels water. The purplish-red underside has a network of ribs clad in abundant sharp spines, possibly a defence against herbivorous fish. Air trapped in spaces between the ribs enables the leaves to float – they are strong and so buoyant that they can easily support the weight of a small child: a mature leaf can carry a load of 45 kg (100 lb) if evenly distributed. In a single season, each plant produces 40 to 50 leaves.

The spectacular flowers last for only 48 hours or so. On the first evening it opens, the flower is white, attracting beetles with a sweet, pineapple-like scent and heat from a thermochemical reaction. At this stage, it is female, open to receiving pollen picked up by beetles from other plants. As they bumble around inside the flower, the beetles transfer pollen and fertilization occurs. Meanwhile, the flower shuts, trapping them until the next evening. During the following day, the flower changes from female to male and produces pollen. When it reopens, the colour has changed to purplish red. The beetles fly off, dusted with pollen, to find another white flower on a different plant and repeat the process. The flower closes up and sinks below the surface of the water, its mission accomplished.

Although not the first Western explorer to encounter this waterlily, Schomburgk was instrumental in introducing it to Europe. With little room in his kayak, he placed a smallish leaf and bud into a barrel filled with brine. The sample eventually made its way back to England, along with 8,000 other plant and animal specimens. It arrived at the Royal Geographical Society five months later, to be named *Victoria regia* by John Lindley, Professor of Botany at University College London. This name, given in honour of Queen Victoria (who had recently been crowned and was also the society's patron) was later superseded. Today, the plant is known as *Victoria amazonica*.

Leading botanists of the day were desperate to get their hands on seeds in order to grow it. Joseph Paxton, head gardener at Chatsworth, was among the first to try to germinate seeds supplied by Schomburgk in 1840, but he failed. It took until 1846 before William Hooker, Director at Kew Gardens, succeeded. Three years later, he had some 30 seedlings to give away, and Paxton was a recipient.

Paxton went on to win a race to coax the plant into flower, building a tank in his Chatsworth conservatory that emulated its native habitat. Yet his fascination did not stop with cultivation. W. H. Fitch's botanical illustrations of the Amazonian waterlily reveal the underside of the giant leaf, showing how cantilevers radiate from the centre and bracing ribs enable the plant to bear weight. Paxton drew on this structure to design a glasshouse for the plant, as well to construct his famous Crystal Palace for the Great Exhibition of 1851. Inextricably linked to the flowering of botanical exploration, the expansion of the Empire and the success of Victorian science and technology, *V. amazonica* is a truly extraordinary plant.

OPPOSITE: *Victoria amazonica* (as *Victoria regia)* by William Sharp, from J. F. Allen: *Victoria regia or the great waterlily of America*, 1854.

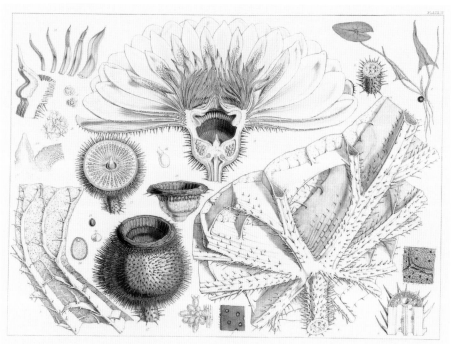

VICTORIA REGIA

LEFT AND BELOW: *Victoria amazonica* (as *Victoria regia*), flower cross-section (left) and plant (below) by Walter Hood Fitch, from W. H. Fitch: *Victoria regia: or, Illustrations of the royal water-lily, in a series of figures chiefly made from specimens flowering at Syon and at Kew*, 1851.

VICTORIA REGIA
Expanded flower

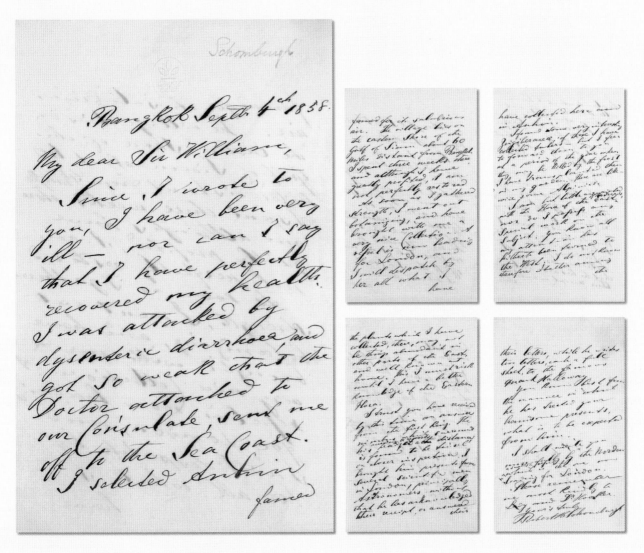

Letter from Robert Schomburgk to Sir William Jackson Hooker, from Bangkok, Thailand, 4 September 1858

In this letter Schomburgk informs Hooker that since he last wrote to him he has been very unwell, suffering an attack of dysenteric diarrhoea, and was so weak that the doctor attached to his consulate had sent him to the coast. He went to Anhin, which lies on the eastern coast of what is now Thailand, about 100 km (60 miles) from Bangkok, and spent three weeks there until he recovered his strength. He then began to collect plants, and sent his collection back to London via a ship from Bangkok, including some very interesting Zingiberaceae tubers. He writes that he is

not very familiar with the flora of the East and does not own any works on the subject. Consequently, he suggests that there may be some plants in his shipped collection that are well known back in London. Schomburgk expects that Hooker has now received a reply from the King of Siam regarding presents given to him from several astronomers in London. Hooker knows the King well, and Schomburgk thinks he will be able to read his response best. Schomburgk concludes by promising to write more fully from the *Morden*, a Swedish vessel now loading for London.

> **38** *Victoria amazonica* (as *Victoria regia*) by Walter Hood Fitch, from W. H. Fitch: *Victoria regia: or, Illustrations of the royal water-lily, in a series of figures chiefly made from specimens flowering at Syon and at Kew*, 1851.

PLANT PLATYPUS:
ANGOLA'S AMAZING TREE-TUMBO
WELWITSCHIA

CHRISTINA HARRISON

If you were told there was a plant that could live for up to 2,000 years, in the unforgiving heat of a desert, with two long, twisted leaves and bizarre-looking cones, you would be forgiven for being sceptical. Yet all this is true of the tree-tumbo or *Welwitschia mirabilis* – a plant so remarkable that it was described by Charles Darwin as the platypus of the plant world.

Welwitschia was first discovered in 1859 by the Austrian naturalist Friedrich Martin Josef Welwitsch, who had been exploring the flora and fauna of Massamedes (present-day Namibe province in Angola). A meticulous, persevering man, he achieved a considerable collection of specimens and described 550 species new to science. On coming across the remarkable plant in the arid plains of southern Angola, he "could do nothing but kneel down on the burning soil and gaze at it, half in fear lest a touch should prove it a figment of the imagination".

On 16 August 1860, Welwitsch wrote to the Director of Kew, Sir William Hooker, who in turn read the letter to the Linnean Society. Welwitsch described this bizarre plant and suggested the name of Tumboa – from the name given by the local people who called it *n'tumbo*, meaning a stump. In 1862, Kew's second Director, Sir Joseph Hooker, formally described the plant in *The Gardeners' Chronicle*. A more detailed paper discussing the plant's significance was published by the Linnean Society in 1863, and it was given the name *Welwitschia mirabilis* – meaning extraordinary – in Welwitsch's honour. Hooker described it as "the most wonderful plant, in a botanical point of view, that has been brought to light during the present century".

Welwitschia has a unique place within the plant kingdom. Botanically, it sits alongside the conifers, cycads and *Ginkgo biloba* within the class of Gymnospermae, and is in its own family of Welwitschiaceae. It grows only in the coastal area of the Namib Desert, where it gathers moisture from the daily fog that rolls in off the sea, and in the rocky hills of Kaokoland to the north. Its two leaves are the only leaves *Welwitschia* grows in its lifetime: should it lose one (from grazing, damage or sandstorm), the plant dies. The leaves, which grow continuously throughout its life, are extremely tough and leathery. They may look tattered, torn and twisted, but this is hardly surprising as they are the longest-lived leaves in the plant kingdom; squirming out like tentacles from a central point, they give *Welwitschia* an octopus-like appearance. Such leaves are an unusual adaptation to a desert environment, where plants usually have small waxy leaves. By exposing a large area to the fog, however, they gain maximum moisture for the plant.

Welwitschia plants bear cones on separate male and female plants. The male cones produce wind-borne pollen that is caught by a sticky substance on the female cones. The seeds only germinate after heavy rainfall, although many are naturally infertile or suffer from a fungus. From the 10,000–20,000 seeds that can be produced, sometimes only 200 have the potential to reach germination.

Today, these iconic plants are relatively common in this area, but grow nowhere else in the world. Some are protected by national parks, and they are valued by the tourist industry as a unique sight of the region. Threats to *Welwitschia* include not only damage by people and storms but also from grazing animals such as oryx, springbok and black rhino, although this usually only occurs in times of extreme drought. Grey's larks have been seen nesting under the plants, and some snakes, lizards and arthropods use them for shelter.

Kew's Millennium Seed Bank has a collection of *Welwitschia* seeds in its vaults to secure the future of this extraordinary species, and a specimen can be seen in the Princess of Wales Conservatory at Kew.

OPPOSITE: *Welwitschia mirabilis* by Thomas Baines, 1861.

THE WELWITSCHIA MIRABILIS, OR PLANT OF HYKAMKOP, SOUTH WEST AFRICA. T. BAINES, MAY 9, 1861.

ABOVE: *The Welwitschia mirabilis* by Thomas Baines, 1861.

LEFT: *Welwitschia mirabilis* by Walter Hood Fitch, from *Curtis's Botanical Magazine,* 1863.

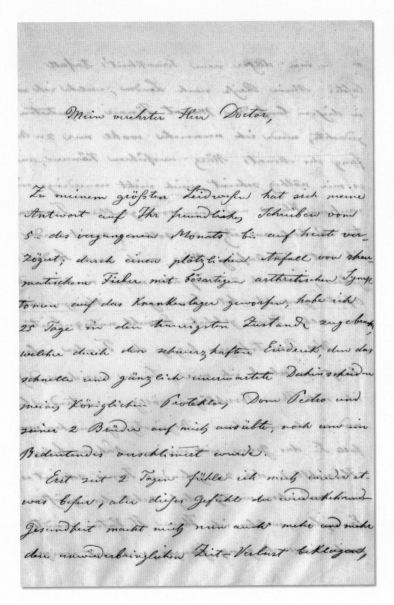

First page of a four page letter from Fréderic Welwitsch
to Sir Joseph Dalton Hooker from Lisbon, 5 January 1862

Welwitsch writes to Hooker about his health and the death of Dom Pedro, his patron. He states he will come to London in March and bring his botany collection from equatorial Africa. He mentions Tumboa, and that he will send another drawing, also that he is honoured to have the genus named after him. Welwitsch has a friend in Cabo Negro who will send him fresh samples of the plants from Africa on the next steamer. He writes about wood specimens and that he has many African species including lianas and some others that he thinks might be useful for the Kew Museum. Finally he mentions Hooker's work on the *Flora of Fernando Po* and his own collections from St Helena. He sends regards to William Hooker and Dr Bentham.

39 *Welwitschia mirabilis* by Walter Hood Fitch, from *Curtis's Botanical Magazine*, 1863.

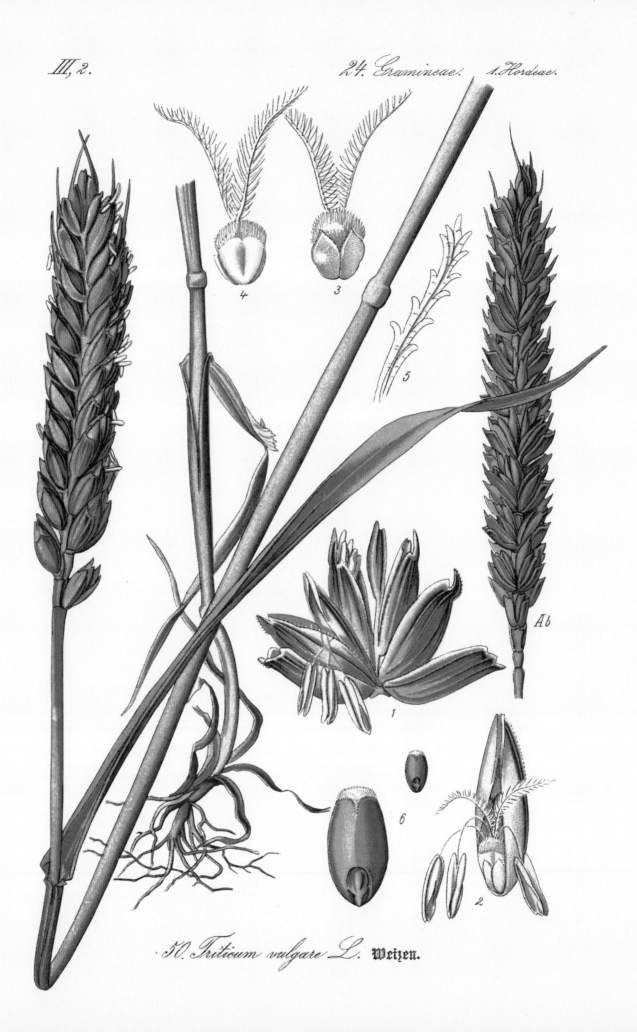

50. Triticum vulgare L. Weizen.

FEED THE WORLD
WHEAT

MARK NESBITT

Today, bread wheat is one of the top three staple food crops, ranked third after maize and rice, and contributing about one fifth of the world's dietary calories. Throughout cooler regions, it is a major part of people's diet, and is used as bread, pasta and cracked wheat, as well as in more local dishes such as soup and porridge. Wheat's importance is also marked by its spiritual significance, as in communion wafers and Easter breads in Christianity, or *aşure*, a boiled wheat dessert made in the first month of the Islamic year and said to mark the landfall of Noah's Ark. Wheat was first cultivated in a narrow strip of mountains, the "fertile crescent", of the Near East, and the story of how it became such a global crop is an intriguing one.

The "fertile crescent" in which wild wheats grew stretched from the Levant via southeast Turkey, northern Syria and Iraq to Iran. Here, about 10,500 years ago, wheat, barley, lentils and peas were among the first crops to be domesticated, as farming began to replace hunter-gathering as an established way of life. As farmers chose favoured forms of wheat from their fields, new ones evolved, including macaroni wheat (*Triticum durum*); these did not have the tough husks of primitive wheats, making it far easier to extract the grain from the chaff. As farming spread eastwards about 8,000 years ago, macaroni wheat naturally crossed in fields with a wild goat grass (*Aegilops tauschii*), resulting in the hybrid that we call bread wheat (*Triticum aestivum*). The genes from goat grass contributed two crucial properties to bread wheat: the ecological adaptations necessary for the plant to grow in areas with cooler climates, and changes to the gluten composition of the grain that gave it its excellent bread-making quality.

Bread wheat did not rise to instant dominance. The tough husks of the primitive wheats einkorn, emmer and spelt protect the grains from disease and pests, a valuable asset for a crop. Spelt, for example, remained the primary wheat of Roman Britain in the early centuries AD. Other cereals, such as barley and rye, offered more reliable yields in years of poor weather. However, by the time of the European colonization of the Americas and Australia in the 17th and 18th centuries, bread wheat had become a major crop of the early settlers. The historian Alfred Crosby has coined the concept of "ecological imperialism" to explain why European settlers displaced indigenous peoples in these temperate regions. Their climate was ideal for European crops (such as wheat) and domesticated animals, and today, the United States and Canada account for about one eighth of the world's production of wheat. In addition, the new colonists brought over European diseases such as smallpox, to which indigenous peoples were not adapted.

For many millennia, farmers informally selected local forms of wheat, known as landraces, for culinary and agronomic properties. Yet their yields remained low: typically about 2 tonnes per hectare (t/ha) (0.8 tons per acre [t/a]) in Britain until the 1950s, compared with 8 t/ha (3.2t/a) now. This quadrupling in yield, matched by similar increases in developing countries, represents one of the great – but unsung – achievements of science in the 20th century. It came about through the "Green Revolution" of the 1950s and 1960s, in which application of chemical fertilizer and, where required, irrigation led to huge increases in plant growth. This initially caused another problem: as wheat plants grew taller they "lodged" (fell over), effectively reducing yields. Plant breeding played a crucial role in resolving this, by introducing dwarfing genes found in Japanese landraces into the new wheat species. These grew much shorter – as can be seen in most wheat fields today – and stayed upright. In 1970, the plant breeder Norman Borlaug, who led the project, won the Nobel Peace Prize for his work on developing dwarf wheat and rice varieties for the Green Revolution.

The challenge of continuing to raise wheat yields to keep up with an increasing global population goes on, complicated by the unpredictable effects of climate change. In the case of wheat, increased levels of carbon dioxide are likely to increase yields, but in many areas, higher temperatures will lead to shorter growing seasons and may also reduce seed set. It is likely that the genes existing in farmers' landraces and in wild wheats will be of value in climate adaptation, and Kew has a key role in a project to map and collect seeds of wild cereals. Bread wheat will continue to be a staple food – but major investment will be required in understanding and using its genetic diversity.

OPPOSITE: *Triticum aestivum* (as *Triticum vulgare*) from O. W. Thomé: *Flora von Deutschland Österreich und der Schweiz*, 1886–89.

Blé Hunter.

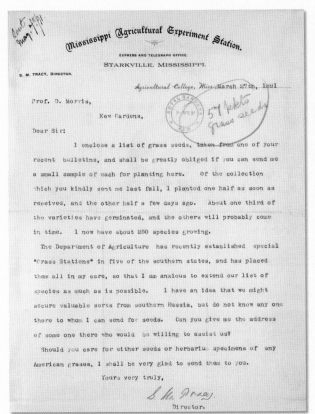

Letter and list of plants from Samuel Mills Tracy to Daniel Morris, Kew's Assistant Director, from Mississippi Agricultural Experiment Station, Starkville, USA, 27 March 1891

Tracy encloses a list of grass seeds taken from one of Morris's recent bulletins and shall be greatly obliged if he can send a small sample of each for planting. Of the collection Morris sent last fall, he planted one half as soon as received and the other half a few days ago. About a third of the varieties have germinated and the others will probably come up in time, and he now has about 250 species growing. The Department of Agriculture has recently established special grass stations in five of the southern states and has placed them all in Tracy's care, so he is anxious to extend their list of species as much as possible. Tracy thinks they might be able to secure valuable grasses from southern Russia, but does not know anyone there to whom he can write and wonders if Morris can help in this respect. Should Morris care for either seeds or herbarium specimens of any American grasses, Tracy shall be glad to send them.

OPPOSITE: Wheat by Eugène Graff from Vilmorin-Andrieux et Cie: *Les meilleurs blés: description et culture des principales variétés de froments d'hiver et de printemps*, 1880.

40 *Triticum aestivum* (as *Triticum vulgare*) from O. W. Thomé: *Flora von Deutschland Österreich und der Schweiz*, 1886–89.

THE AUTHORS

Julia Buckley is an Information Assistant within Kew's Art & Illustrations Collection and joined Kew in 2005 after working in the field of book information. Kew's Illustrations Collection holds more than 200,000 prints, drawings, and paintings ranging in date from the seventeenth century to the present day.

Lorna Cahill is Kew's Assistant Archivist. She has worked at Kew since September 2012, and started her archives career volunteering there in 2008. She has previously worked in the archives of Royal Holloway, University of London, and the Natural History Museum.

Chris Clennett is Garden Manager at Wakehurst, Kew's country estate in Sussex. He has been at Wakehurst for nearly 30 years and is trained in horticulture and botany. He combines managing the ornamental and botanical collections with scientific research and is author of the Kew monograph on *Erythronium*.

Aljos Farjon is a conifer specialist and Honorary Research Associate at the Royal Botanic Gardens, Kew and is also Chair of the IUCN Conifer Specialist Group.

Gina Fullerlove is Head of Publishing at the Royal Botanic Gardens, Kew. She has a first degree in Biological Sciences from the University of London and undertook research training in Biological Anthropology at the University of Durham before embarking on a career in publishing.

Lauren Gardiner is a Career Development Fellow and specialist in palms and orchids in the Conservation Science department at Kew. She works with local communities in Madagascar on species and habitat conservation.

David Goyder is a botanist in Kew's Africa and Madagascar team. He studies plant diversity in tropical Africa and has particular interests in historical collections from the continent, and the milkweed family Apocynaceae.

Tony Hall is an Honorary Research Associate at Kew, where he previously worked for almost 30 years as Manager of the Alpine and Bulb Unit. He has an interest in woodland, alpine and bulbous plants, but especially irises.

Christina Harrison is the Editor of *Kew* magazine at the Royal Botanic Gardens, Kew. She has a degree in Plant Ecology and Environmental Science, and a masters in Garden History. She is the author of *Kew's Big Trees* and co-author of *Treasured Trees*.

Christopher Mills is Head of the Library, Art and Archives collections at the Royal Botanic Gardens, Kew. Previously he was Head of Collections and Services at the Natural History Museum. In his current role Mills led on the development of the Shirley Sherwood Gallery of Botanical Art and the renovation and conservation of the Marianne North Gallery and its collection. He oversaw the development of the new Library at Kew and currently is continuing a programme of activities to improve, conserve, digitize and make all the collections more accessible and better known.

Virginia Mills is the Project Officer for Kew's Joseph Hooker Correspondence Project, which is making Hooker's letters available online to highlight his importance in the history of science, botany and the development of Kew Gardens. Virginia has previously worked at the Natural History Museum.

Mark Nesbitt is Curator of Kew's Economic Botany Collection. Trained in botany, agriculture and archaeology, his research interests include the history of plants and people, colonial botany in the 19th century, and the management and use of ethnobotanical collections.

Lynn Parker is Assistant Art and Artefacts Curator in Kew's Library, Art and Archives. She previously worked in collections management at the Victoria and Albert Museum and with anthropological and photographic collections at the Pitt Rivers Museum in Oxford.

Tony Rebelo works at the South African National Biodiversity Institute at Kirstenbosch. He has published research in optimal conservation strategies in the Cape Flora, pollination of proteas and restoration of Fynbos, as well as documenting southern Africa's vegetation types.

Martyn Rix is a renowned horticulturalist, and author of many books including *The Golden Age of Botanical Art* and editor of *Curtis's Botanical Magazine*, founded in 1787.

Kiri Ross-Jones is Kew's Archivist and Records Manager. She has managed Kew's archives since 2006, prior to which she worked in the archives of the Victoria and Albert Museum, London and the National Maritime Museum at Greenwich. Kew's historical archives contain about 7 million sheets of paper and document the history of the Gardens, as well as botany more generally.

Marcelo Sellaro works as a Collections Horticulturalist in the Nurseries department at the Royal Botanic Gardens, Kew. He has a degree in agronomy from the University of São Paulo, and his research interests include the ecology of epiphytic vegetation, including bromeliads.

Anna Trias-Blasi is a Research Fellow at the Royal Botanic Gardens, Kew. She trained in plant biodiversity and taxonomy at the Royal Botanic Gardens, Edinburgh and Trinity College Dublin before joining Kew in 2010. Her research interests include the taxonomy, systematics and conservation of Asian members of the grape family (Vitaceae) and selected petaloid monocots, large-scale plant conservation priority-setting and climbing plant diversity.

Maria Vorontsova is Research Leader of Integrated Monography in the department of Comparative Plant and Fungal Biology at the Royal Botanic Gardens, Kew. Her research is focussed on grasses and in particular tropical African diversity.

James Wearn currently works in Science Education at Kew and is leading Kew's First World War Centenary commemoration project. He is an ecologist and military historian and has carried out fieldwork across the world and delved into numerous archive collections unearthing long forgotten stories.

Richard Wilford is Head of Garden Design and Collection Support at Kew. His main interests are bulbs, alpines and herbaceous perennials and he is the author of *Tulips; species and hybrids for the gardener*, *Alpines from Mountain to Garden*, *Growing Garden Bulbs* and *The Plant Lover's Guide to Tulips*.

Joanne Yeomans is a Gallery Assistant at the Shirley Sherwood Gallery of Botanical Art and Marianne North Gallery at Kew. The Shirley Sherwood Gallery of Botanical Art is the first gallery in the world solely dedicated to botanical art and Joanne has worked there since it opened in 2008, having previously completed an undergraduate degree and master's degree in History of Art at the University of Warwick.

Daniela Zappi is a cactus expert at the Royal Botanic Gardens, Kew, working in the Conservation department. With a degree in Biological Sciences and a PhD on Cactaceae, she has travelled extensively in South America researching and supervising students in the cactus and coffee families.

GENERAL READING

Nancy Broadbent Casserley, *Washi: The Art of Japanese paper*, Royal Botanic Gardens, Kew, 2013.

Helen Bynum and William Bynum, *Remarkable Plants That Shape Our World,* Thames and Hudson, 2014.

Ray Desmond, *The History of the Royal Botanic Gardens, Kew*, 2nd Edition Royal Botanic Gardens, Kew, 2007.

Mike Fraser and Liz Fraser, *The Smallest Kingdom*, Royal Botanic Gardens, Kew, 2011.

Patricia Griggs, *Joseph Hooker: Botanical Trailblazer*, Royal Botanic Gardens, Kew, 2011.

Jane Kilpatrick, *Fathers of Botany: The discovery of Chinese Plants by European Missionaries*, Royal Botanic Gardens, Kew and University of Chicago Press, 2014.

Tony Kirkham and John Flanagan, *Wilson's China: A Century On*, Royal Botanic Gardens, Kew, 2009.

W. John Kress and Shirley Sherwood, *The Art of Plant Evolution*, Royal Botanic Gardens, Kew, 2009.

Marianne North, *Official Guide to the Marianne North Gallery*, 6th edition, Royal Botanic Gardens, Kew, 2009.

Lynn Parker and Kiri Ross-Jones, *The Story of Kew Gardens in Photographs*, Arcturus Publishing, 2013.

Michelle Payne, *Marianne North: A Very Intrepid Painter,* Royal Botanic Gardens, Kew, 2011.

Martyn Rix, *The Golden Age of Botanical Art*, André Deutsch, 2012.

Shirley Sherwood and Martyn Rix, *Treasures of Botanical Art: Icons from the Shirley Sherwood and Kew Collections*, Royal Botanic Gardens, Kew, 2008.

Kathy Willis and Carolyn Fry, *Plants From Roots to Riches*, John Murray, 2014.

Masumi Yamanaka, Christina Harrison and Martyn Rix, *Treasured Trees*, Royal Botanic Gardens, Kew, 2015.

Miss Drake del.

Epidendrum vitellinum.

INDEX

Fin.

2   3   4   5

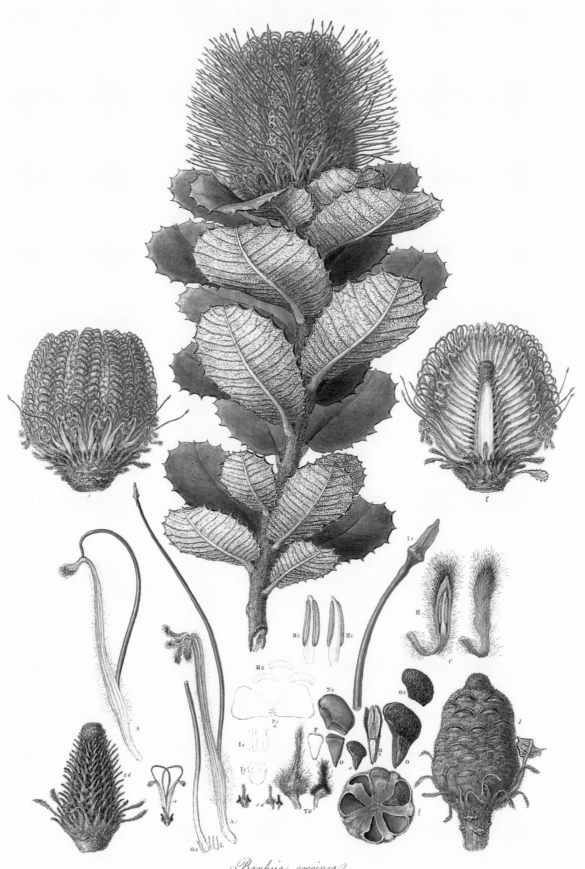

Banksia coccinea.

Brown prod. fl. nov. holl. p. 394. n. 17.

The Market
Dec.? 29 1841

From the Meadow near ? ?? ?

4 *Ananas comosus,* from M. S.
Merian: *De metamorphosis
insectorum Surinamensium,* 1705

Echinocactus longihamatus Gal

Nach der Natur gezeichnet von T. Gürke.

Tafel 9.

J. Curtis del San 1825.

Camellia japonica var.

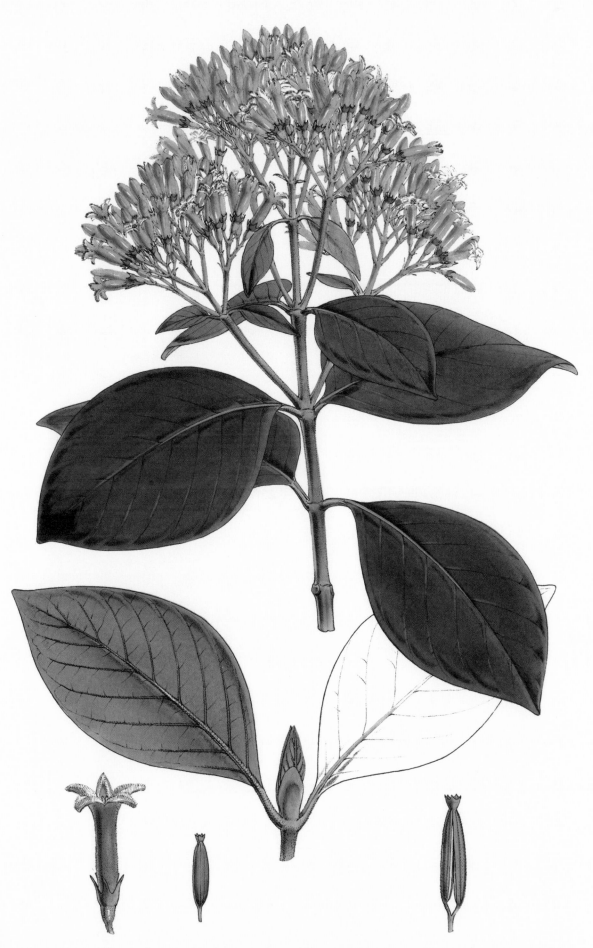

CINCHONA ERYTHRANTHA, Pavon.

Citrus Aurantium melitense.

8 *Citrus* x *aurantium* var. *melitense* by Pancrace Bessa, from F. Mordant De Launay and J. L. A. Loiseleur-Deslongchamps: *Herbier général de l'amateur*, 1817–27.

DATURA CORNUCOPŒA.FL.PL.

9 *Datura cornucopaea*, from W. Robinson:
*The Garden. An illustrated weekly journal
of horticulture in all its brances*, 1894.

Fritillaire Impériale.

P. J. Redouté.

Chinese name
白菜樹 *Peh*
kwo
shoo.

Salisburia adiantifolia

12 *Ginkgo biloba*, watercolour on Chinese paper, commissioned c.1850 by the botanist and plant hunte Robert Fortune as part of a set of 23 tree portraits.

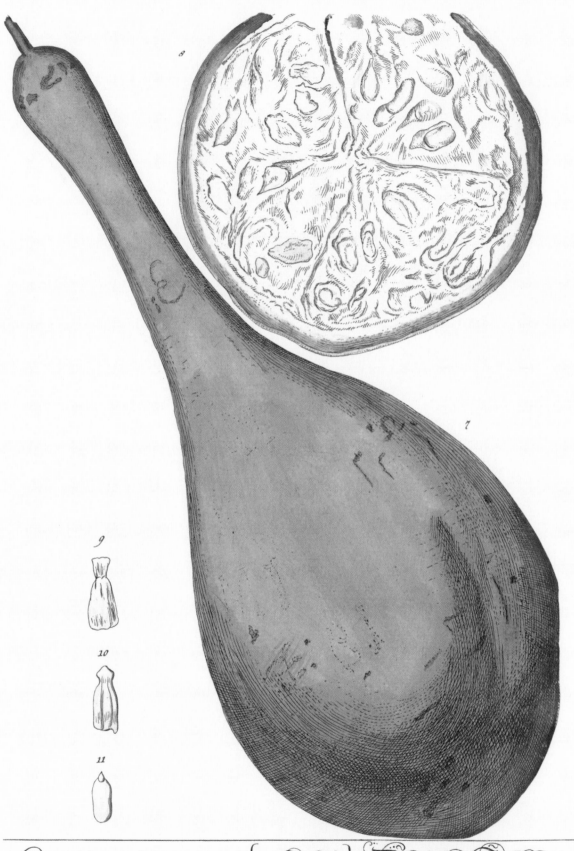

Cucurbita lagenaria . { 7.8. Frucht 9-11. Saame } Flaſchen Kürbis .

VITIS vinifera.   VIGNE cultivée. var. *Bourdelas noir*.

Gra--mineae.

Saccharum officinarum L.

IRIS bulbosa latifolia, caule donata. Bauh. pin.

Samara
~~*Nymphaea rubra*, R.~~
Nelumbium speciosum

19 *Nelumbium speciosum,* from the Roxburgh Collection, Kew, late 18th/early 19th century.

MAGNOLIA CAMPBELLII, H.&T.

Magnolia campbellii by Walter Hood
Fitch, from J. D. Hooker and W. H. Fitch
Illustrations of Himalayan plants, 1855.

一種 紫色の物

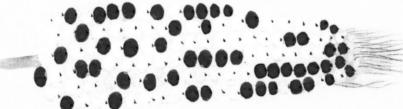

一種 二日色の物白色

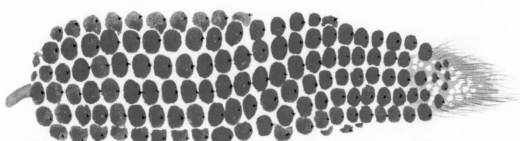

一種 白色の物

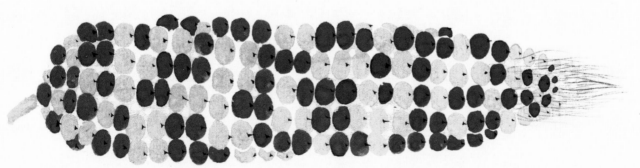

一種 赤色の物

一種 紫色白色相雜る物

Nepenthes northiana by Marianne North, 1881. Named after the artist by Sir Joseph Hooker.

Papaveraceae.

Papaver somniferum L.

W.Müller n d Nat

23 *Papaver somniferum*, from
F. E. Köhler: *Medizinal
Pflanzen*, 1890.

Vanda cœrulea.

Cypr. Fairieanum Lindl.

Palmae
(Cocoineae)

Taf. II. Cocos nucifera L.

27 *Pandanus or screw palm covered with climbing plants, near the Kongone Canal of the Zambesi* by Thomas Baines, from D. Livingstone: *The Zambesi Expedition of David Livingstone*, 1858

BROUSSONETIA papyrifera .   **BROUSSONET** à papier *pag. 26*

Passiflora caerulea by James Sowerby, from the first volume of *Curtis's Botanical Magazine*, 1787.

Paeonia daurica

Protea speciosa with golden-
breasted cuckoo by Marianne
North, 1882.

Rhododendron Hookeri Nutt.

ROSA Gallica.   ROSIER de France.

33 *Rosa gallica* by Pancrace Bessa, from H. L. Duhamel du Monceau: *Traité des arbres et arbustes*, Nouvelle édition, 1819.

Strelitzia reginae by Franz Bauer, from F. Bauer: *Strelitzia depicta, or coloured figures of the known species of the genus Strelitzia from the drawings in the Banksian library,* 1818.

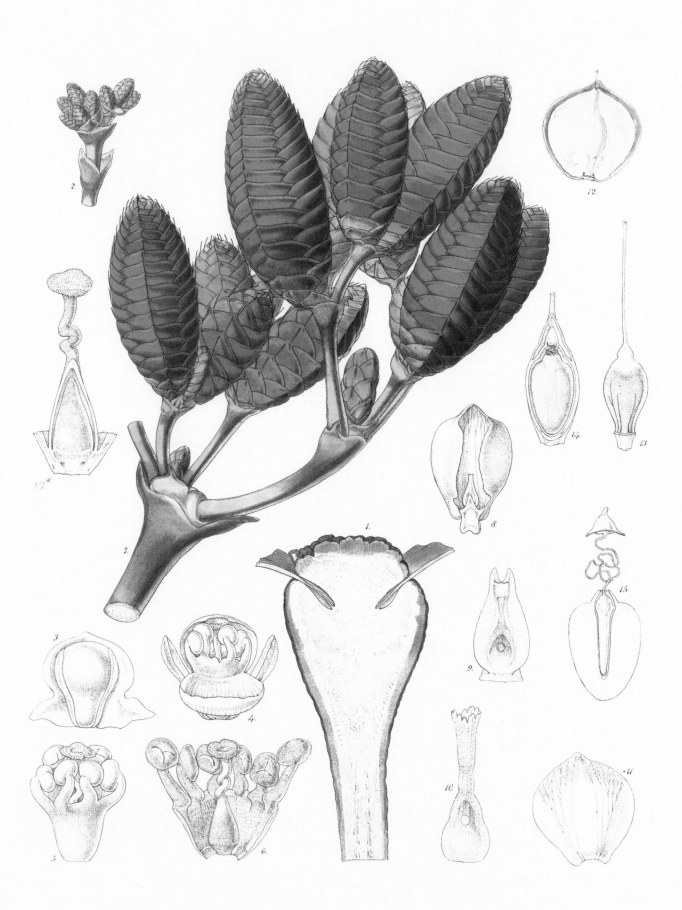

39 *Welwitschia mirabilis* by Walter Hood Fitch, from *Curtis's Botanical Magazine*, 1863.